C0-ACN-596

The Language of My Heart

An Amish Girl's Journal

Illustrated by Susie Wagler

PATHWAY PUBLISHERS
Route 4,
Aylmer, Ontario
N5H 2R3

THE LANGUAGE OF MY HEART

Printed in U.S.A.

A NOTE FROM THE AUTHOR

With considerable misgiving I submit this manuscript for publication. How I wish it were possible to simply hide myself and say, "No, I did not write this story. You see, it does not have an author."

For though I am using a pen name, I am afraid those folks who know me will peer right through my flimsy camouflage and find me out — expose me before all the personal thoughts and feelings expressed in my journal.

Something else worries me even more. Suppose people think they recognize other characters in the story. Suppose they feel hurt or insulted.

I admit that the Lois in the story is basically myself and that much of the story has been taken word for word from my own journal. But I hasten to add that many details have also been changed. In pursuit of anonymity I have borrowed from the experiences of many other people, and I have not hesitated to transpose characters and rearrange personality traits.

Therefore it is my plea that no one attempt to identify any characters or events in this book.

Ah, little book of mine,
I hold you in my hands and sigh,
Afraid to let you go.

"Lord, let no harm result
From words I've written here;
May they honor Thy name
And not degrade it.
May they be a blessing
And not a curse.
An inspiration, and not a mockery.
Let them not be
Mere entertainment,
But words which may enrich
The lives of those who read them.

"And as this book goes various ways
To friends I've never met,
Bless each soul
With the sunshine
of Thy love."

- "Lois Yoder"
September 6, 1988

"By the time I reached the schoolhouse I was almost shaking."
(Page 31)

January 1,

DEAR JOURNAL,

Hello!

I'm lost. I don't know how or where to start in this big, empty-paged journal. Journals are just like other things in life- be they shoes, clothes or friends. When they're new, they're stiff and uncomfortable. I hate anything that is stiff and uncomfortable, because it makes me feel ill at ease, and I hate to feel ill at ease. I want to be myself, and to feel free to do and think and write as I please, especially in journals, so my dear new journal, be prepared to be scribbled in, in all manners of ways.

For some reason, I'm in the mood to take an inventory of myself, family, home, friends, and life in general. Perhaps a brand new diary does justify an introduction and a few explanations.

I'll start with myself. My name is Lois Yoder. I am eighteen years old. I am the owner of a pair of blue-gray eyes, a high forehead, high cheekbones, unmanageably wavy light brown hair, a crooked nose, pointed chin, and two medium-sized dimples. At least that is what I gather from occasional peeps in the mirror and assorted remarks from well-meaning people. I am of average height, 5' 4", and to my great woe- slightly plump and stocky. My figure used to be a great worry to me, but I think I have attained enough maturity to realize that it is only a matter of pride to care so much about one's looks. Besides, when all's said and done, I guess I'm not so very bad-looking. Not a stunner like my sister Joanne, to be sure, but not so ugly after all.

If Mom would chance to read this last paragraph, she would be sure to deliver a lecture that I already know by heart, beginning with something like this, "Now listen, Lois, looks aren't important at all. It's the inside that matters. People aren't going to think less of you because you don't have a pretty nose or a trim figure, or —" and so on and so on. I'm agreed, Mom, one hundred percent. Beauty of the heart is beyond comparison, I know, and yet most people admire and covet good looks.

But- I'm getting way off track. As for my character and personality, I just don't know. In a way I wish I could get someone else's honest opinion, but perhaps I wouldn't have the courage to hear it.

I have often wondered what kind of girl I actually am. I'm not really bashful, but then again, sometimes I am bashful, painfully so. I am outgoing at times, and at times quiet and withdrawn. Sometimes fun loving and silly, and then — sober and solemn as an owl. I'm usually a home baby, but every now and then I get the "wanderfoot" and long to get out and go, to experience new adventures and meet new friends.

I've got my share of bad habits. I'm awfully absent-minded, forgetful, disorganized, and generally harum scarum. This of course is a trial to Mom's clear-cut, precise way of doing things.

I also laugh a lot, smile a lot, cry a lot, which must mean that I have not yet found the control button to my emotions.

I kind of like to write. Nothing amounting to much, just little scribble-de-roos that work off my steam when I'm upset, ease my sorrow when I'm mourning, and build up my joy when I am glad. It seems most of my spare time is used in writing letters to my friends and scribbling in journals. There is always a limit to my time, it seems, and half a hundred unfinished projects clamoring for my attention. Maybe when I get to be middle-aged and live all alone in my old maid's house, I'll find time to do the things I've been dreaming about.

When I was a little girl, I went through a gardening craze and built great dream castles, with me in my old maid's hut, surrounded by rows and rows of beautiful flowers and vegetables growing lushly outside my front doorstep. Now these great gardening dreams have evaporated, and so I must admit, have the old maid dreams- somewhat. Maybe not completely. I am a woman, with a woman's instinct to love and be loved. When the right one finds me and I find him, I'll be willing to serve him hand and foot, and share with him, the bitter and the sweet. But that hasn't happened yet. Until it does, I am happy and satisfied with the daily joys and challenges life offers me now.

And so, in conclusion, I would say that in spite of a few oddities and strange streaks, I'm just an average, ordinary girl, faced with the struggles, temptations, joys, and sorrows that every girl encounters. In thinking and looking back over my eighteen and a half years, I can see so many flaws in my character, so many times I have made mistakes. May God help me be a better person in the future. I heard the clock strike twelve downstairs just now. Imagine— starting out a new journal, writing till midnight- and all about myself. I've just discovered my worst fault— self-centeredness!

January 8,

Here I am again, and I'm still in the sketching mood, although a whole week has passed, and it is late tonight and I am tired.

I have a good view of my family tonight as they lounge in their various chairs, or sit propped up on the woodbox behind the stove. So I'll dig right in, describing them.

It would probably be proper to start with the head of the house. Right now he's nodding on his rocking chair, with his newspaper sliding to his feet. He looks very much like a wise philosopher, (in spite of his nodding) with his graying beard, balding head, and the dignified spectacles on his nose. Calm, steady, and easy-going- the kind of person you can depend upon. I used to think there wasn't a thing he couldn't do or didn't know, but now that my own wisdom has picked up a wee bit, I can see that he is only human after all.

Mom is small and a little round. She has snapping brown eyes and a quick temper. She also has the softest heart in the world and will forgive a person while she is still in the process of giving him a tongue lashing. She is very unselfish, which I sometimes fear has resulted in selfish children!

Dad says she used to be a belle. I believe it,

because she is still something of one.

David is next in line, but he isn't here, because he left home almost a year ago to be wed to his petite wife, Mary Anne. They live about two miles from here.

David is a lot like Dad. Calm, steady and quiet. He's shy around strangers, but full of teasing and fun at home. We miss him.

And then- Joanne- my gorgeous twenty-year-old sister. Right now she is trying on a new light-blue dress and looks like a princess royal. I'm jealous of her half of the time, because she has all the qualities I've always been hankering for. She is small and slender, she has a doll-like face with two large sky-blue eyes in the middle, a perfectly shaped nose, and a fair complexion, with just enough color in her cheeks to make her look dazzling. And yes, she's even got the golden hair that curls in ringlets around her forehead. What's more, she has a personality to match. The kind that makes people swarm around her like bees to a honeypot. Oh, I used to have a fierce time with myself, and with the green-eyed monster Jealousy, until I realized how immature that was. I think I've finally accepted Joanne as she is, and myself as I am. I've stopped trying to be Joanne and am just trying to be me. At least I hope so.

Joanne and I are great pals. There is not much about her that I don't know, because she is such an obliging person. She'll tell me anything she knows.

Poor Joanne's surrounded with suitors. So far, none of them have touched the magic spot in her heart— or mine. I always tell her "he" will have to pass my inspection as well as hers.

I've got to keep moving or I'll never get done.

Okay- enter Prince Charming, Master Mischief-maker and Monkeyshiner. This is my brother Stephen, of whom I am very proud and often provoked at. He really is very handsome, though he has common gray eyes a little like mine and a big nose with a decided curve in it. He's tall and thin like Dad, but he's got Mom's activeness and zip. He is very obstinate and loves to argue, but other than that he is about all you could ask for in a brother.

Hannah is five years younger than I. She is shy and quiet, and very well-behaved. Steve claims he got all the badness and left only goodness for her. She is also very industrious and can make the work fly.

Nathan is seven and a little charmer, with his dark curls and sparkling brown eyes. He has an intellectual streak and spends hours poring over books above his age level. He's only pint sized though.

So that is the story of the Yoder eight, or at least part of the story.

We live on a hundred acre farm, with Daisy, our red and gold collie, our dozen cats, eighteen cows, and who knows how many pigs, horses, and hens.

Our white house is perched on top of a long sloping hill. The lane is hemmed in by evergreens on both sides. It leads to the road at the bottom of the hill. On the other side of the road there is a twin hill to ours, and nearly at the top there's a twin to our house. Our closest neighbors live there, the Dan Fisher family.

They also have a girl who is almost my twin— Annie. Annie has always been a part of my life, and seems more like a sister than the neighbor's girl.

The rest of the family has long deserted me for the luxury of their beds. It's getting to be rather creepy down here in the kitchen all alone, so I guess I'll go join them.

P.S. (Jan. 10,) (IMPORTANT!) I have left unrecorded the youngest of the Yoder clan. Small blame to me, for she was only born this morning at 1:35 to David and Mary Anne. Her name is Elizabeth, she weighs six pounds, she has a red face, a head full of black hair, a tiny nose, and a big voice. At least that was my impression of her tonight when I went to the hospital for my first peep at her. I must wait to write more until I learn to know her better.

January 12,

Sunday evening- Steve, Joanne and I just got home from the singing at Uncle Levi's. Joanne has already snuggled into bed. She says I'm queer to scribble in this journal when I could be sleeping. She can't understand my need to write in diaries. (Can't really blame her.) The less writing she has to do, the happier she is. When she needs to get something out of her system, she talks, whereas I write. Strange-- to think that we're sisters and yet put together so differently.

Tonight at the singing I sat in a convenient out-of-the-way corner where I could watch everybody and no one thought to watch me. Between singing and behaving myself, I made a few observations.

Observation number one: Joe Miller likes to look at Joanne very well. He took the liberty of smiling at her every possible chance he got. Perhaps he is the one, I don't know. He is like Joanne in some ways. He is one of the handsomest boys I've ever seen and he has an enchanting personality. I like that side of him very much, but there is another side that is hard to explain. Not that he's really wild, but every now and then little bits of his character come to the surface and it makes me wonder how deep and strong he actually is.

I've seen it in the way he combs his hair, the kind of jokes he relates, the remarks he makes about people, the songs he sings, his swagger and the sometimes haughty expression on his face. Is it personal convictions that keep him in line, or is it just to stay on the good side of folks?

That sounds judgmental. I really do like him and I'd be glad if my fears were all wrong.

Observation number two: Joe is not the only one interested in Joanne. Ervin Troyer is interested too— and he's serious. He's not the fickle type, and when he pays attention to a girl, it means something. Which is sad, because I'm afraid he doesn't stand a chance. He is the exact opposite of Joe— short, rather "unhandsome", and very quiet and shy.

I'm sure he is nice enough underneath, but I still don't think he and Joanne would be a good match. Joe and Joanne would probably fit better. (Even their names match!)

I'd better get to bed if I plan to be a half-decent hired girl tomorrow at Davids. I'm a bit scared because always before it was Joanne who worked away—and I have no experience in that line. Oh, I can cook and bake and clean, but it will be different doing it for someone else.

January 14,

This finds me up here in one of Davids' stuffy little upstairs rooms. I've just finished discovering a hard, unwelcome truth. I am a great big baby. The two hot tears that made their mournful way down my nose just now are sure proof of the fact. Imagine, an eighteen-year-old only two miles from home, in her own brother's house, and she is homesick!

It actually isn't so bad. In David and Mary Anne's presence, I try to be cheerful and sing and laugh and talk like my usual self, but I will be glad when I can go home again. It's not that I don't enjoy it here— I only keep wondering what all I'm missing at home.

It's a funny thing to say, but I wish Mary Anne wasn't quite so perfect. I haven't learned to relax around her yet. I feel like such a clumsy goose, compared to her easy calm self. At home when I burn the bread black, or my cake's a flop, or I spill the milk on the floor, I accept my family's scolding and teasing as a part of routine. In fact, I think I kind of enjoy it, at least the teasing part. Here at Davids, Mary Anne wouldn't say a word about my failures and flops, but I can just imagine what she thinks.

Bathing the baby is another of my trials. I am sure any normal person would not understand why I should dread such an envied and enjoyable task, but I do. I think I would like it if I could do it in some hidden corner, where Mary Anne could not see my awkward movements, and if naughty little Elizabeth would not get such a great enjoyment out of making a dunce out of her poor auntie. The minute I sit down beside the stove with her, she waves her little fists, kicks her little heels, opens her tiny mouth and screams incessantly until I feel like doing the same thing. By the time I'm finally done dabbing her all over with a warm, wet cloth, rubbing her dry, and fumbling with her clothes, I'm in a nervous sweat.

But I should not write so about Elizabeth, as she is the dearest, cuddliest thing I ever saw. I think she and I are going to be great pals when we grow up. There seems to be something special between us already- (bathing experiences excluded!) I've been imagining her through all her growing up stages—smiling and cooing, then crawling and walking and talking. I'll have to tell her someday what a trial she was to me when I tried to bathe her.

January 20,

DEAR JOURNAL,

There's something not quite right with me tonight. I can't say what—some blue mood creeping over me, I guess. It's a restlessness and dissatisfaction with myself and life in general.

All my eighteen years I have lived a life of comfort, never known hunger pains or a lack of warm clothes. I have grown up with the feeling of being loved by family and friends. I have been taught the story of God's love from babyhood, by word and example. Indeed, I have been blessed many times over, so much more than I deserve. My life so far has been a full and a happy one, and yet— it has been a struggle. Sometimes I wonder if I am making very much progress in my spiritual life. Is this the way it will always be? This struggling to do right—failing, asking God for forgiveness—and failing again. When I think I am making progress in one area, I find I've gone wrong in another.

When I was younger, I thought it would be easier to be good and wise when I was older. I used to dream of doing something great and noble and earthshaking. I even thought I would like to be a writer—and make people laugh and cry and see through my eyes the beauty and tragedy of life.

What vain castles in the air! I have grown more realistic, and faced the fact that the world is a wicked, wicked place, and that one lone insignificant individual like me can do little to change it. Especially, when that one lone individual needs help and encouragement herself.

But still, there is that vacancy in my heart—that restless longing to do something. Was I put on the earth merely to wash dishes and clean and bake and sew all my life long?

February 10,

Long time no write. I'm exceptionally lazy these days, nearly as bad as Joanne. The last several evenings I've been picking up a book after supper and reading until I am sleepy.

So I'm pretty good at making predictions. Sure enough, this past Sunday evening, here comes Steve with a message from Joe to Joanne, asking to take her home. Joanne begged for a week's time to think it over, and Joe behaved like a gentleman. He even told Steve to say that he is sorry if he is rushing her too much.

So—what now? Today is Tuesday. In five more days, it will be Sunday and Joanne will need to have her answer ready. The problem is, she doesn't know what she is going to say. She actually does think a lot of Joe, (naturally, since he's the type of boy girls fall for) but she isn't sure that he is the kind of person she would want for a husband. Besides, Dad and Mom kind of discourage her. I am glad I'm not in her shoes, though being her sister is almost as bad.

If Joe wouldn't be so utterly likable and charming!

February 12,

The answer to Joanne's question came tonight in an unpleasant way. I'm too tired to write all the details, but we heard it from a reliable source. (His own sister Mary told Annie Fisher and Annie told me.) Joe had a date with a girl in Ohio when he was visiting there only three weeks ago. Mary said he really does want Joanne, but the Ohio boys wanted him to take someone home, so he thought he would— just for the fun of it.

Imagine the nerve— coming back home and asking Joanne right away. At least it helped Joanne make her decision. She said if he's not more serious than that, he'll have to look somewhere else.

Poor Joanne. Her heart is as soft as margarine, and she can hardly bear to turn him down, even with this new mark against him.

February 18,

I did some sewing today, besides helping with the baking. Hannah came home from school with red-rimmed eyes. Mom spotted them right away and began interrogating her, which greatly added to her misery. She finally got the story sobbed out. All the other girls were going somewhere for the night tomorrow evening, except for her. They hadn't even invited her or told her about it. She had found one of their secret notes, and asked one of the younger girls, who told her that she knew what it was all about but that Hannah was not supposed to find out.

Joanne and I exchanged amused glances behind our weeping sister's back. She is a dear, but she is not very far-sighted or presuming. Evidently she forgot that tomorrow is her birthday.

A well-taped note in Nathan's dinner bucket, addressed to Mom from the upper grade girls, confirmed our suspicions.

I wish Hannah would not be so sensitive and easily hurt. I know I am too much so myself, but Hannah is even more that way. And she's so shy.

Joanne wrote a letter to Joe, explaining her refusal, and Steve delivered it after the singing on Sunday evening. Sure wonder what his reaction was.

March 30,

Steve and I tramped through the woods today, operating on maple trees, inserting spiles and hanging up pails. The spring air got into my blood and I acted like a tomboy. I hopped and skipped and (ssssshhh-) even climbed a tree. It is so wonderful to get out there in the wide open world, so free and full of fresh clean air. I get tired of breathing stale, second-hand kitchen air, day in and day out, and of doing the same old pokey jobs, quilting, sewing, mending, cleaning, and making meals. I always come through the winter with pale cheeks, weak muscles, and added pounds. Of course, the latter bothers me the most.

I wish I would learn to like housework better. It worries me sometimes. Now, when I get that penned-up, choked feeling, I can wheedle Mom into letting me run out and help the men. But suppose I end up being a housewife someday, with a bunch of children to tie me down. Maybe I'll have learned the secret of patience by that time. (But of course, I might never have to worry about being a housewife in the first place.)

I've been trying to decide whether I would accept a teaching job if the schoolboard asked me. I doubt that Miriam Beiler will be teaching our school next term, since everybody's expecting a wedding announcement either this spring or this fall.

I think I would like to try teaching, but the very thought makes the shivers go up and down my back. Suppose I can't and end up a failure.

April 3,

We quilted most of today. Mary Anne and Elizabeth came to help us. I sat very primly and stitched away, just as though I was not aching to smash the whole works flat and run outside to help Steve cook sap.

David and Mary Anne stayed for supper, and just now they walked over to the neighbors and left Elizabeth here till they come back. She is snuggled up in my left arm, watching me with her big, blue eyes. She's getting to be a real little charmer and we've all lost our hearts to her. It does me good to see how fond David is of his little girlie. She's the apple of his eye already.

Now she's on the verge of dropping off to sleep.

She looks so pure and innocent, lying there with her eyes half-closed. Dear little baby girl. I think it's a pity she has to grow up. How nice if her little face would never lose its sweet innocence, or her eyes their clear, untroubled gaze.

May God protect you, my dear little niece, and help you to grow up to be strong and brave and true.

April 19,

Right now, I'm glad I haven't got Joanne's attractive face, enchanting mannerisms, or whatever she has that's making the boys all bow at her feet. She got a letter from Ervin Troyer today, asking for her friendship. Joanne let me read it, and it's a real nice letter. I don't know whom I pity the most—Ervin or Joanne.

April 20,

Well, what do you know? Joanne just told me of her decision to accept Ervin's offer of friendship. I'm still gasping and trying to let the fact soak through to my shocked brain. I guess I thought Joanne was going to turn down boys the rest of her life.

But Ervin Troyer? If someone would have asked me a week ago who I thought Joanne would choose, I probably would have said the least likely one was Ervin. I guess I don't know my sister as well as I thought I did.

I blamed her for saying yes only because she's tired of saying no. She scolded me good and properly for that and asked me why I acted so shocked. I said, "Because you're so pretty and he's so hom—" and then I stopped because I suddenly realized how mean I was being. She really did scold then, and asked me just how immature I was, to dwell so much on looks when I knew that that part wasn't important at all. I melted then, and asked her to pardon me, and she melted and said she was sorry for getting so heated up. She said the reason she did was because she was still trying to persuade herself, and she needed encouragement, not discouragement.

"And Lois," she said. "You know you can't say a valid word against him. He is nice all the way through. I've thought so for awhile already, though I didn't dare tell you. I'm afraid we girls have been putting too much emphasis on looks. I must admit I had a pretty tough battle when I got that letter, because Ervin isn't really my 'dream man'. But I decided that if looks and a winning personality are more important to me than a fine Christian character, there is something wrong with me. I feel a lot better since I made that decision, so don't you go and get me all mixed up again."

I didn't know Sis could get so earnest about something. I'm ashamed of myself. I guess Mom's lectures never really penetrated very far, even though I thought they did. I have known all along that someone like Ervin would make a better husband than Joe, and yet I probably would have preferred Joe to Ervin, just because God formed one young man's features more perfectly than the other.

Where did I ever get the notion that Joanne would have to end up with a dazzling knight of some kind, just because she happens to be kind of pretty herself?

June 20,

Sigh, sigh, sigh. I must record a most exasperating, humiliating and humorous afternoon. I still feel like a watch wound up to its limit, with my muscles taut and tense, and my hair still damp from the sweating I've done.

It began with Mom and Joanne's heading for Uncle Levis after dinner to help them pick strawberries. After they drove out the lane, I glanced at the clock, rolled up my dress sleeves, and felt very ambitious. I was to get rid of a worktable full of dirty dishes, do a small pile of mending, redd up the house, and clean some berries for supper. That was the assignment Mom had given me but I knew I could get a lot more work done than all that.

I thought of the fact that it was Dad's birthday, and that we had barely taken time to acknowledge it so far. I decided to go on a baking spree and turn out a banquet of a supper.

So I began hurrying the dishes through the suds, trying to decide my menu as I did so. I finally settled on pizza (Dad's favorite), potato casserole, lettuce salad, a birthday cake and ice cream. The fact that it would take a lot of hurrying to get it done made it all the more challenging.

There! Dishes done. I glanced at them, drying on the rack, and hoped they were all clean.

Now for the most detestable job of mending. I sat down hurriedly at the sewing machine, hoping there would be no major tears.

I barely got the sewing machine humming when things started tangling up and getting stuck. I fumbled around for a long time, trying to get it working.

Finally my patience and the needle snapped at the same time. I rummaged through all the drawers and could not find another needle, so I gave up mending as a bad job.

I made the cake next, and stuck it into the oven to bake. Then I mixed the pizza dough and rolled it out. About three quarters of an hour later, I took out a surprisingly presentable cake, stirred together some icing and set it on the stove to boil. Then I decided to start on the ice cream so I could hide it down in the cellar as a surprise for the family.

I ran out to the barn with a pitcher to skim off some cream, and to get some milk. And then, I came to my senses and slid to an abrupt halt outside the milkhouse door. The milkman! Of course, he had been there this forenoon and taken every drop of our milk.

When I plan something, I can hardly bear to give it up. I opened the barn door and took a quick look, even though I knew that at this time of the day all the cows were at the farthest end of our farm, munching grass and chewing their cuds. But surprisingly enough, there was old Blackie standing in the corner, looking sad and lonely. Without stopping to wonder what she was doing at home, I hustled her into the barn to her stanchion, grabbed a pail and began milking her.

A few minutes later I rushed into the kitchen with my pail full of foaming milk. I was almost knocked back out the door by the stench and smoke rising from the stove in black billows. My icing! Through the smoky blackness, I could see it bubbling merrily over the sides of the kettle and making great splashes on top of the stove.

I grabbed a hot-pad, pulled off the kettle, and burned my hand. Then I tore open the windows and managed to get the stove cleaned and the air cleared somewhat, when I heard a knock. Still holding a cool rag to my burned hand, I walked to the door and opened it. There stood Mary Anne, looking cool and fresh as ever, with Elizabeth in one arm and a shopping bag dangling from the other.

"Hi, Lois," she said sweetly. "Could I leave Elizabeth here for an hour or two while I drive up to Miller's store and get some groceries? David said they're fixing the road, and I'd feel safer without Elizabeth in my arms, when I go past all those gravel trucks and road graders."

I gulped and tried to look pleased as I took the squirming Elizabeth from Mary Anne's arms.

Now what was I to do? I couldn't very handily take Elizabeth outside with me to make ice cream because there was no place to put her. At length, I made a nest for her with blankets on the kitchen floor, dragged the ice cream freezer inside, stirred and beat together my ice cream, and suddenly remembered, like old Mother Goose, that I had no ice!

By this time I thought my nerves had had about all they could take. I couldn't leave Elizabeth in the house alone while I ran all the way to the ice house to get a chunk of ice. Just then I spotted Steve's tan shirt disappearing into the shed. I hastily tied on Elizabeth's cap and dashed out to catch him.

I panted out my story to him and he listened kindly and patiently, until I mentioned milking Blackie. Then his mouth dropped open and he gasped, "Blackie?

Blackie! Lois, you _didn't_ use Blackie's milk for that ice-cream!"

I was beginning to feel dizzy. "Why not?" I demanded.

"Well, my dear sister, that cow's milk is contaminated. She's sick and the vet treated her this morning. I thought you knew that. You'll have to dump that whole freezer full of ice cream. You sure are a great one to get yourself in a mess." Steve looked at me gravely as though he was trying to be sympathetic, but his eyes were twinkling and his lips twitching, and I knew he wanted to laugh.

It was not hard for me to decide what _I_ wanted to do. I stared at Steve dumbly for a minute, then quickly turned around before he could see my flood of tears. "This is too much," I rebelled as I stumbled to the house with Elizabeth, who was now crying at the top of her lungs (perhaps in sympathy).

Evidently it was not too much. A few minutes later I looked out the window, and beheld to my utter horror, a white and blue van nosing into our lane. Unfamiliar faces framed by bonnets and hats were peering from the small mud-splattered windows. I glanced desperately at the hurricane kitchen, at the unfinished pizzas on the table— to the ice cream freezer mess in the corner, and vowed that whoever they were, they must not step inside.

I glanced into the mirror and was dismayed even more to see the marks of recent tears still visible. Just then I saw Steve walking toward the van and I breathed a deep sigh of relief. A few minutes later the van drove out the lane and Steve appeared at the door, his face still wearing that grave, amused look.

"Lois," he said solemnly. "How strong are your nerves?"

I groaned. "Oh, Steve, please hurry and tell me what next."

"All right, calm down. It's nothing at all. Those folks went to school with Dad and they would like to come back for an early supper in about an hour."

I sank into a chair. I didn't care for another crying spell, so I started laughing helplessly instead. It seemed so ridiculous all of a sudden. How could so many things happen in one afternoon?

I'm getting tired of writing, so I will only add that I survived, thanks to Steve's kind help and Mom's and Joanne's when they finally came home about fifteen minutes before our visitors returned. Our supper consisted of potato soup, cake without icing, and mashed strawberries, instead of casserole, salad, pizza, a fancy birthday cake and ice cream.

Mom would probably say that the purpose of such an afternoon was to teach me several much-needed lessons. Namely, not to take such big bites, or to be so determined to push my own way through when I've had plenty of warnings that things won't work out. And I have also learned that in circumstances like this one, it is better to laugh than to cry, better to look at the humorous side and relax.

I happened to think of something right now. I took several bites of that poisoned ice cream while making it. If Steve wouldn't be sleeping already, I'd ask him when I'm expected to get sick.

July 3,

I've just come upstairs, after spending an unusually leisurely evening browsing through a box of Dad's and Mom's old letters. It was almost like being transferred to a different world. Lots of letters from their cousins, uncles, aunts, parents, grandparents, and school friends. When they wrote those letters, many of them were as young or younger than I am now, in the prime of their lives — the generation of the day. Now they are old men and women, (though Dad and Mom would say they're still young) and a new generation has arisen. It makes me feel a little queer to think if the world stands, and I live to be fifty or sixty, I'll be living in the middle of a new generation — with folks not even born now.

How surely time goes on, and new generations rise, fade, and are gone. How surely the end comes for us all.

Lord, would that I could do something with this brief span of mine, something that will stand in eternity. Sometimes it seems as though I'm hardly doing anything at all.

July 8,

In glancing over the last several pages of my journal, I see that I haven't mentioned the fact that the school board came knocking at our door several weeks ago. When they left, I was hired as their teacher, for better or for worse.

I don't know what to think, but I hope that with God's help I can do it. Perhaps it will help me get rid of this restless feeling of mine.

July 25,

I'm tired, and yet not relaxed enough to think of

dropping off to sleep right away. So I'll resort to my good friend, the journal.

This is Sunday evening again, by the way, and I can hear Ervin and Joanne chattering like two magpies downstairs. Who would have ever thought Ervin could talk like that?

I like Ervin more and more as time goes on, and I rather think Joanne does, too!

Life surely is full of changes—some happy, some sad, and some happy and sad at the same time. For instance, I'm glad that Joanne is happy, but I still resent the change Ervin's appearance on the scene brings with it. Joanne and I have always been very close, even when I almost let jealousy come between us. Now, I just know she is changing. Sure, she loves me as she always has, but she doesn't <u>need</u> me nearly as much, because she's got Ervin. Give her a couple of months and she'll be a lot worse. Give her a couple of years and she'll probably be married, which will mean another disruption, and a gaping hole in the family.

Same story with my good friend Annie. She's different since she started going with Eddie. She has to be, because her interests have changed.

Boo hoo!

I can't figure myself out. I think I'm beginning to like Joe a little too well. I'm trying not to, but perhaps my efforts are not genuine enough. I thought it would be very hard to trust him again after the way he let us down a few months ago, but he seemed to take Joanne's refusal so hard that I forgave him almost right away. The way he acted for a few weeks made me wonder if there was not a lost little boy behind his usual bluff and cocksureness. I felt, and still feel, very sorry for him, but maybe I'm showing my friendly feeling too much. I hope I'll never stoop to flirting like some girls do. I don't want to be self-righteous or critical, but I do wish such girls would try harder to stay in their places.

July 28,

I walked down to the schoolhouse to see if there was anything I could do to get ready. I tinkered around a bit, but didn't do anything worth talking about. I'm getting worried. Suppose I get into something I can't handle.

I will have twenty pupils, grades one to seven. There are no eighth graders. I know the pupils well, but I don't know if that is a point in my favor or not.

I guess I will go along to the annual teachers' meeting on the sixth and seventh of August.

August 10,

My dear journal, if you only knew how much smarter and wiser I have become since I picked you up last, you would wonder at me! I have been to a Teachers' Meeting! I have seen and observed all kinds of people, I have listened to talks and sermons and advice delivered by people from all over the continent, until my head was ready to burst. Thankfully it did no more than ache a little.

If I could follow all the advice I gleaned the last several days, my school should be a model school. But I fear my efforts will be pretty green, especially the first while.

Am I prepared for the job I've accepted?

Dear God, there is this load on my heart and on my shoulders. You know all about it — about this fear of the unknown and of the work that lies ahead of me. I cannot do it alone. I don't know how. Give me the wisdom, the love, and the goodness that is lacking in my life. Teach me how to teach your little children.

August 19,

I've got a problem.

I must stop flirting with Joe. Yes, that's right. I might as well call it flirting, in spite of my bland remarks only a few pages back.

What makes it hard is that I'm not the only one at it. Joe is, too. I don't think he's serious. He likes any attention he can get from me and he likes to lead me on. And though it makes me blush to admit it, that is what I am doing, too.

I care for Joe more than I wish to admit. Those brown eyes of his make my heart go flip flop. But deep down, I know that the feeling I have for Joe is not the true kind of love that stands the test. Nor do I feel that I can really respect and trust him.

No, when I am honest with myself, I know that Joe is not the "dream man kind of person" (as Joanne would term it) that I am looking for. My "dream man" will have to be someone I can trust enough to give him my heart. Someone I can lean on, who will help me be a better person, and strengthen my faith in God.

Maybe I'm asking for too much, but as long as I can't have that kind of trust in Joe, I had better not pretend that I do.

I hope I can stick to my resolutions.

August 24,

I forgot to mention that a new family moved in — Sollie Zooks. I went over to help them get settled today. They have a daughter, Ruth, and she's the prettiest girl I ever saw, even prettier than Joanne.

I wish I could overcome these feelings of pride and jealousy once and for all. As soon as I saw Ruth, I knew I wouldn't feel at ease around her. I was sure she knew she was pretty and was probably looking down her nose at ordinary, commonplace me. I felt awkward and unsure of myself, though I tried not to show it.

It was silly to feel that way, I know, but I don't think it was all my fault. She acted sort of stuck-up.

Why do I get such strange notions? I feel the same way when I'm around Mary Anne, and even sometimes Joanne. They make me feel so unattractive and clumsy. As I've said before, I guess I'm not all that bad-looking, but somehow, I don't have the grace, charm, and enchanting airs that folks like Ruth have.

Actually, what does it matter? I wish I could stop being so concerned about myself.

Only a week till school starts. I still have a lot of things to do.

September 1,

My very first day of school is now history.

This morning I woke up at four and couldn't sleep. At 4:45 I got the rest of the family out of their beds and we chored and had breakfast before sunrise. I packed my lunch, and poked around a little till it was time to go, and all the while, my stomach felt queerer and queerer.

After many fatherly, motherly, brotherly, and sisterly good wishes and bits of advice from Dad, Mom, Joanne and Steve, I bravely started out the long lane and down the road in the direction of the little white schoolhouse in the distance. I started out with a fair amount of confidence, but with every step I took, I seemed to leave some of it behind. And with every step I took, the more tempting it was to turn around and run back. By the time I reached the schoolhouse I was almost shaking. I knew that I could not start out the day like that, so I dropped to my knees beside my swivel chair and stayed there until a calm courage took over. I had to think of the song, "Tis so Sweet to Trust in Jesus."

The rest of the day went real well, I thought, except for a few mind disturbers. I had prepared some quizzes with questions such as, "Did you like school last year? Do you think you will like it this year? What rules do you think are important for a happy school?"

I thought most of the pupils' answers showed exceptionally healthy attitudes, but there were a few that dampened my spirits. Peter Mast, and Henry and Isaac Knepp (brothers) wrote that they didn't like school last year, and they didn't think they would this year either. Peter thought that "No rules" was the best answer to the last question.

Peter seems to be something of an outlaw, or perhaps he's only pretending to be one. Henry and Isaac have been friendly and likable enough so far, but I have a feeling they might not have extra strong backbones.

I must write about my first graders, and then I will

have to head for bed before I collapse in my chair.

I have four — three girls and one boy. Two of the girls are twins, Martha and Mary Zook, (Sollie Zook's) and I think I will have to make them wear name tags the first few days. They look like little miniatures of Ruth, the same elfin faces, soulful eyes and graceful airs.

And Jerry — he's got the most angelic face of all. If he actually is as good as he looks, I shouldn't have any trouble with him. (Incidentally, he looks like his older brother, Joe Miller.)

I'm at least knee deep in love with those three already, but I'm afraid it'll be harder to have the right feeling toward Ellen, the youngest of the four. She is big and heavy-set, with a perpetual scowl on her face and bossy, dislikable ways.

But oh, I'm so tired, so completely drained of strength and ambition. And tomorrow's another day.

September 5,

I've made it through my first week of school. I've been too tensed up to enjoy it very much so far. I must be more of a bundle of nerves than I realized. I can't even eat properly anymore and have already lost 3-4 pounds in five days.

One thing that has surprised me is the pupils' seeming acceptance of me as their teacher. They actually take for granted that I know as much as my teacher used to know when I went to school. And I must admit that bustling around, answering hands, giving assignments and checking lessons, makes me feel like the real thing.

I thought I knew my pupils fairly well on the first

day of school, but I've learned a lot more about them in a week's time. I've learned that Jerry is not as angelic, or Ellen as dislikable, or Peter as much of an outlaw, as I thought they were going to be. I wonder what all else I will learn in the next eight months.

September 7,

Face it, Lois. You've made a big mistake, a big bad, bad mistake.

I could cry and cry. In fact, I'm at it.

Oh, why did I ever even as much as look at Joe? I didn't think he was serious, but evidently he was, because tonight he asked to take me home.

I don't know when I was ever before put on such a spot. I thought I couldn't say no, and I was not ready to say yes. I never dreamt it would be so hard to turn him down. I almost didn't but then I decided that I had been cruel enough. I couldn't accept even one date when I knew in my heart that I didn't really want him in the long run.

Some folks would probably say I should have given him a chance. Why didn't I? I know that I have many shortcomings and weaknesses myself, and right now, I feel downright wicked. But it's like Dad said when Joe asked Joanne, "Shortcomings and weaknesses are easy to overlook, if the person behind them has the right attitude and the sincere desire to do better." It's Joe's attitude toward life in general that scares me.

Perhaps Joe would have asked me anyhow, without any encouragement from me. Maybe he wasn't serious, and only wanted a date 'for the fun of it.'

I almost hope so, so I won't need to feel so guilty.

September 11,

I had a bad run-in with Jerry today. He's got the stubbornest streak I ever saw in a little boy.

Just before recess, I noticed that the floor surrounding the first graders' desks had a very messy appearance. I frowned, sent Martha to fetch the waste basket, and told the other first graders to pick up all the paper. I had turned my back and was returning to my desk when I became aware of Martha's little hand waving frantically in my face.

"Yes, Martha," I said, looking down at her and wondering what the shocked look on her face was all about.

"Teacher, Jerry said he's not going to pick up his paper.""

I turned quickly in Jerry's direction, still in time to see his head moving vigorously from side to side.

I stepped over. "Did you pick up your papers, Jerry?"

"No! They aren't mine."

"That doesn't make any difference. I want you to help pick up those papers. O.K.?"

"No." Calmly. Defiantly.

It was my turn to be shocked. I glanced around at the wide-eyed, watching children and nearly panicked. What was I to do now? One thing I did know, I was not going to give in to this daring little boy.

Evidently, he had made a similar resolution. I dismissed the children for recess and Jerry and I settled down to a tough battle of wills. He kept staring mournfully at me with those great, big, innocent eyes of his, but he did not give up.

I thought I could not spank him — not during the

second week of school, but finally I saw there was no loophole by which to escape. Besides, even if he gave up now without the spanking, I felt he deserved a pretty stiff punishment for defying me so openly.

So I did what I thought I could not do. I, Lois Yoder, gave my first spanking.

It was all it took. Jerry looked so small and miserable that I took him in my arms and held him. To my surprise, he snuggled right up to me like a scared little bunny and sniffed out the words, "I'll - I'll pick up the paper now." As he had given up, I helped him pick up the paper and we resumed school, the best of friends.

But for how long? I've seen enough of Jerry the last week and a half to realize that he has some deep-seated emotional problems — problems that won't be solved in a day or two.

He reminds me so much of Joe. So easy to love, and yet —

I'm feeling blue about everything tonight.

September 21,

If I thought I had the blues the other evening, I have them tenfold worse tonight.

Today Annie and I had a good talk. She wasn't going to tell me, but I soon sensed that she knew that Joe had asked me. I kept working at her until she finally told me that Joe had been talking with Eddie and told him that he can't understand why I told him off when I acted as though I wanted him. He said he would have expected flirting from some of the other girls, but not from me.

My first impulse was to rise to the defensive.

After all I hadn't really gone out of my place. And the last several weeks before he had asked me I had pretty well ignored him, true to my resolution. And the reason I had thought he wasn't serious was because I knew that he liked to talk with just about any girl.

But I've taken my heart to court and found it guilty. I was in the wrong, and I'm ready to humbly admit it. It was all my pride that brought this trouble — a subconscious desire to seek attention from the boys, and to be popular like Joanne. I was flattered to think that Joe would even notice me. And while I am not mean enough to want to turn down boys, I still figured it would be ego-lifting, a few stars added to my crown to have him ask me.

It is bitter medicine to admit all this. I haven't been so humbled for a long time.

To think that boys such as Joe, who like to flirt themselves, respect the girls who don't.

God, forgive me my pride and my mistakes, and help me be a better example from now on.

Forgive me too, Joe.

September 28,

It hurts me to have Joe avoid me so deliberately. When I meet him on the road, he barely looks at me. Quite a contrast to his former almost over-friendly ways. I wish we could still be friends.

I've got a feeling my next problem will be Sammy Fisher, Annie's brother. Annie's one of the best friends I have, but I hope that neither Sammy nor anyone else thinks it is because I'm after him. Sammy's kind of nice, and an old school friend, but

I find him rather uninteresting.

Perhaps it is all my imagination that he's beginning to act as though he cared for me.

I wonder sometimes if there is a Mr. Right for me. Of course, I'm still young, (I'll be nineteen next month) but somehow, I can't make myself believe that I could ever care enough for any of the boys I know, to marry one of them. Perhaps my old maid dreams will come true after all, (though the woman in me cries out — "Perish the thought!")

October 9,

I haven't mentioned school for a long time, mainly because we seem to be under a spell, and I'm afraid to mention it for fear of breaking the spell.

Oh, I have my daily trials, but so far they have had solutions.

I wish I knew how strict to be about some of those little things — such as turning around, whispering in line-ups, monkey-shining. I hate the idea of nagging, but how soon I catch myself at it.

They are a fairly easy group to handle though, and I love them all dearly, even Peter and Ellen.

Can you imagine — Ervin and Joanne are already making wedding plans! This coming spring sometime. Joanne seems to be happy though I don't think I would be, if I knew that I had to leave this happy, comfortable home so soon, and face hordes of new responsibilities and adjustments — just for the sake of one man!

I guess I'm sort of strange. One minute I'm letting on I'd never want to get married, and the next I'm wondering when my knight in shining armor will come on the scene. The truth is, I'm not sure what I want. I think I would like to have someone special to love, and a home of my own someday, but I want to keep it in the safe, faraway future for a good many years.

October 10,

Today was my birthday. My pupils overloaded me with small presents and greetings, and were extra obliging and helpful. I guess this is one of the rewards teachers are always talking about.

Really though, I can't seem to love teaching as much as some teachers let on they do. I love the children, yes, but all the responsibility is irksome to me. Monday mornings are especially bad. It's hard to get back under the yoke and face five whole days of hard work and stress before another two days of carefree relaxing. Perhaps I am too immature or not really a teacher at heart.

October 30,

I can hardly believe it. Eddie quit Annie after nearly a year of courtship. Just like that, without any warning.

I never saw Annie so heartbroken. Nor have I ever felt so helpless. I think I must comfort her somehow, but how?

I'm really down on boys tonight. I don't think there are very many to be trusted.

Hark ye, a boy will have to be pretty wonderful before I'm willing to risk going through something like that.

November 5,

Perhaps I'd better apologize for being so hard on Eddie. Annie said today this break-up is just as hard on him as it is on her. The reason he didn't say something sooner was because he couldn't bring himself to hurt her like that. Annie sure has a loyal heart. She wouldn't say a word against Eddie for anything. I guess if she can forgive him. so can I.

Ruth Zook came to school today to fetch her brothers and sisters because it was raining. On an impulse I asked her if she would like to come to our place some evening and stay for the night. She accepted quite readily and we agreed on tomorrow evening.

By the way, Ruth and I are good friends now. I still feel drab compared to her, but it doesn't bother me much anymore. Perhaps I'm slowly, slowly growing up.

November 7,

I'm tired tonight. I guess I'll put the blame on Ruth. If she wouldn't have been such an interesting conversationalist I would have gotten my sleep.

Steve sure didn't act like himself last night. I'm suspicious about some things.

There was one part of our conversation that I thought was sort of interesting. We were talking when suddenly out of the blue, Ruth said, "You know, Lois, it's hard to believe that I was so afraid of you the first day I saw you — you know the day you came to help us move."

I gasped. "W-Why would you have been afraid of me?"

"Because as soon as I saw you I thought you were so pretty and had such nice ways. I was sure that you knew it, and that you wouldn't want to have anything to do with a commonplace girl like me. In fact, I thought you acted a little stuck-up!"

"But, Ruth," I said in astonishment. "That's exactly the way I felt about you!"

What funny girls we are. I'm sure though, that if I were as pretty as Ruth, I'd know it.

Thursday will be the wedding day of former teacher Miriam Beiler and Andy Keim. Wonder how it would feel to have such a great change coming into one's life.

Sammy will probably ask to take me to the table in the evening. I don't look forward to it, frankly speaking.

November 9,

Oh, God, what can I say? I am hurting all over, aching with emotions that cannot be expressed. All day I have been walking around in a daze, trying to accept this new tragedy.

It must be midnight, at least. I went to bed a few hours ago, but I could not sleep. All the happenings of today kept marching and remarching through my mind. Perhaps if I write for awhile, I will feel better.

This morning I woke up in a grouchy mood. It was blustery and stormy, and for some reason I dreaded facing another long tiresome school day. I snapped at Steve and Joanne and talked back to Mom. At last Dad rebuked me in his calm, gentle way — which should have brought me to my senses. I flared up instead, flung something over my shoulder about no one trying to understand me, grabbed my dinner bucket, and slammed the door behind me. I wasn't halfway out the lane before I started feeling ever so sorry, but I was too proud to go back and apologize.

I had an awful morning at school. The children were extra trying and I felt miserable and guilty. I kept telling myself that I wasn't fit to be a teacher if I couldn't act in a more grown-up way than I had that morning.

About dinnertime I glanced out the window and saw Steve drive into the schoolyard with Candy and the surrey. I remember wondering what he could want at that time of the day, but then I realized that here was my chance to apologize, and I forgot all else.

I hurried out to the entrance without waiting for his knock. "Hi Steve," I started to say, and then a shock went through me. I had never seen such a look on Steve's face before. Instantly, my thoughts went wild. Something must have gone wrong at home. Someone had been hurt or -- or --

We both just stood there for what seemed like an endlessly long time, until finally I managed to choke out, "Steve, tell me quick. What - what's wrong?"

"There - there was an accident."

An accident. I caught hold of the door knob and my knees wobbled. My stomach got the queerest feeling, as though it had dropped out from beneath me. Then something had happened. Who? Dad? Mom? Joanne? Hannah? David? Mary Anne? Elizabeth? One by one, their faces flashed before my eyes. And just as fast came the accusing memory of my unkind words to them such a short while ago.

Steve was going on in a shaky voice that didn't

sound like his voice at all. "It's-it's Dan Fisher. He was kicked by a horse. He's still breathing, but the doctor said it won't be long."

Dan Fisher — Oh, what relief. Nothing dreadful had happened to my family after all. They were all safe and alive. And then the reality struck home. Dan was hurt badly; he might have died already. My thoughts flew to his wife Mary, to Annie, to Sammy, and to four of my pupils, seated just inside the door.

"Is there no hope?" I asked in a whisper.

Steve shook his head. "I came to take the children home. Please, Lois, will you tell them?"

I stared at him in horror. "Oh, Steve, how can I?" I asked desperately.

"Someone will have to. Don't tell them that—. Just - just tell them that he's hurt badly." He turned to go and then stopped.

"Lois."

"Yes."

"I-I found him." Then he was out the door.

I stood there in the entrance, struggling to get back some composure. I couldn't believe it all at once. Our good-natured, helpful, energetic neighbor...

Numbly, I went in and broke the news to the children, trying to keep my voice from trembling too much. Then I helped them into their clothes and walked with them out to the buggy. The looks on their faces haunt me still.

I didn't know whether I was expected to keep school going or not, but I decided to stay until we got further word. Perhaps there had been a mistake and Dan wasn't as seriously hurt as they thought he was.

An hour later, Sollie Zook stopped in and said that

Dan had died only a few minutes after reaching the hospital.

I dismissed the children through blinding tears. It touched me to see them so subdued — walking on tiptoes and talking in whispers.

I found out more details when I got home, though details didn't seem very important just then.

Dan had been in the house only a few minutes before it happened. His last words were to two-year-old Jacob. He said, "Be a good boy for Mamma," left the house, and started shoeing one of their horses. About the same time, Steve came walking over to borrow a vise grip. He found Dan lying on the floor, unconscious, a big bump on his head. He ran in to the house and told Mary and Annie and then sprinted up to the neighbors to call the ambulance. (Sammy wasn't home at the time.)

I have never seen Steve so shook up before. Everyone is. Dan was everybody's friend.

It is so beautiful outside right now. It was stormy all day, but now everything is calm and quiet. From the window I can see the full moon, shedding its golden light over the snow-covered world.

I wish my heart were as peaceful. I know I shouldn't question God's wisdom, but it seems so unfair. It is so hard to think of that poor, fatherless family. I wonder if they are also tossing and turning in their beds, unable to sleep.

It is so hard to grasp. Only this morning I saw Dan walking around in the barnyard, saw him wave one of his friendly, hearty waves. I can't imagine him any way except alive, alert and active.

I wonder what time it is. I must go to bed and

try to get some sleep. There are some difficult days ahead of us.

November 12,

Today was the funeral.

The other day I was so mixed up. I couldn't seem to accept the tragedy as part of God's plan. On Tuesday, when the undertakers brought the body home and we went over to view him, I wished I wouldn't have to go. But when I saw Dan lying there, so peacefully serene, I changed my mind. Somehow, God's presence was in that room, assuring us that He would take care of the grieving family, that this was His will, and that someday we would understand.

I think Dan's death has brought many hearts closer to each other and to God. It seemed as though God was taking this way to talk to us, and to remind us again what life is all about.

For what is life but a vapor? The end will come for all of us, and in eternity it will not be important that some were taken before the rest, only if we were ready.

But oh, I wish I could comfort Annie and the rest of the family somehow. Oh God, be with them in their grief, whisper to them of your love and goodness, and give them courage to go on.

November 21,

Another beautiful day. Church was at Sollie Zooks today. Usually I would have stayed for the afternoon, but I had something of a headache and took that for an excuse to come home with the rest of the family.

An aspirin and a short nap took care of the headache and now I feel fine.

I've been staring across the November fields, just thinking. Wondering and pondering the ways of life and death — the mystery that no man can grasp. What is life, and what is death, and life after death? God grant that someday I may understand.

It's now over a week since Dan's death. I've done a lot of thinking in that time. I have wondered many times since that moment when Steve came to school and told me about Dan — what if death had claimed one of my family? It could have, just as easily as it claimed Dan. I have always tried to push such unpleasant thoughts away, but this shock was too close to home to try to pretend that it couldn't happen to us.

And if there had been a tragedy in our family, I wonder if I ever would have been able to forgive myself for the way I acted that morning.

Or suppose I would have been the one killed. What a sad memory my last words would have left for my family.

And — I have to go back further than that. What have I done with my nineteen years of life to have made it worth the living? Would I have been ready to die?

I have always wanted what is right, and was baptized upon the confession of my faith. To be honest with myself, I guess I've always considered myself a pretty decent kind of person. But suddenly, my smug feeling is gone. I am seeing myself as I really am — with a nature so sinful and vain that I'm plunged into depths of despair. I have been too much of a half-hearted Christian — my life so far has been too hollow and meaningless.

In looking over the pages I have written the past few months, I see that even my journal shows evidence of this. My thoughts have been too taken up with boys, my appearance, and other people's opinions of me. I have been too self-centered, and have forgotten the important things in life. That is why I had such a battle with jealousy, why I wanted to be as popular as Joanne, and why I have made a lot of other mistakes.

It seems so vain and senseless now. When I die, people will not remember how I looked; it will be the deeds that I have done that will linger on.

Dear God, it is my prayer that from now on, I may strive for a nobler goal. First of all, that I may learn to love and know you better, and then to help spread that love to others. Let me forget myself. There are so many people who need kindness shown to them, a smile, a helping hand — that I cannot take time to dwell on my own selfish desires. I can't do much, but Jesus, I pray from the bottom of my heart, you who are our perfect example of compassion and love, help me to do the little that I can do.

"Take my hands and let them be,
Consecrated, Lord, to Thee,
Take my hands, and let them move,
At the impulse of Thy love.
Take my will and make it Thine,
It shall be no longer mine;
Take my heart, it is Thine own,
It shall be Thy royal throne.

Take my love, oh Lord, I pour,
At Thy feet its treasure store.
Take myself, and I will be,
Ever only, all for Thee."

My God, forgive me all my transgressions, and make me as pure and white as the snow outside. Be with me in the days to come. In Jesus' name, Amen.

December 6,

I'm feeling discouraged tonight. I reread the last few pages of this journal just now, the ones I wrote about two weeks ago. I felt so close to God then, and so sure that I would not fall into my old rut of being selfish and self-centered and snappy with my family. But I keep being those very things. Perhaps it is partly because I have set my goals higher, that I am so much more aware of my faults and seem to be losing ground instead of gaining.

Take today for instance. I woke up feeling slightly out of sorts with the world in general. God seemed far away and I didn't bother spending very much time on my knees. And the whole day turned out to be a miserable failure.

While doing the Saturday cleaning, I took a survey of our house, and noticed once more the contrast between it and the houses of some of the folks in the community.

I looked with disdain at the faded, worn-down little worktable, and mentally compared it with Sollie Zooks' varnished and gleaming one, with the row of uppers reposing above it. Then I glanced at the floor. It is the kind that looks dirty all the time, even after a thorough scrubbing, and it has several big, jagged cracks and occasional stubborn stains dotting it here and there. Next I looked over the stove I was cleaning. It stood there meekly, as though ashamed of its chipped enamel and battered sides. I looked at the walls, the windows, the furniture, and everything had that plain, well-worn look.

Ugh. What a homely house. I was thoroughly ashamed of it just then, and was just wetting my lips to tell Mom so, when I decided to change my tactics. I haven't lived with Mom for nineteen years without learning that to fly into a huff is the last thing to do if you want to win her to your way of thinking.

So I began sweetly, "Mom, wouldn't it be nice to have this house fixed up a bit for Joanne's wedding? Not much, you know, just a little paint here and there, and perhaps a new kitchen floor put in —" I didn't dare mention getting a new worktable or a new stove just yet, all in one breath.

Mom looked at me as though she thought there was something the matter with me.

"Why," she said. "What's wrong with this house the way it is?"

I forgot my winning-over-plan. "I'd say what's right with it!" I spoke indignantly. "Why, Mom, just look at it!"

Mom looked, with the air of one surveying a palace. Needless to say, I lost that battle. And, I also lost my temper, and Mom ended up giving me a lecture worth listening to.

I resented being scolded like a little girl, and made sure Mom knew it by setting my lips in a straight line and wearing my most injured look. While I was still in this state of mind, Joanne came tripping down the

"Mom looked, with the air of one surveying a palace."

stairs with an injured look on *her* face.

"Lois," she said darkly, "did you wear my dress to school this week? I had it hanging in my closet, ironed and ready for church tomorrow. And just now I found it *lying on the closet floor*, all rumpled and dirty."

I have to admit that I have a bad habit of neglecting my own clothes, and of borrowing someone else's in desperation. I *had* grabbed Joanne's dress on Friday morning in a weak moment, as it hung in the closet, neatly ironed and ready to go. But I had been uncomfortable in it all day because it had been both tight and too short, and because I dreaded Joanne's reaction when she would find me out. And then when I had come home from school, I had hung the dress on a hook and forgotten all about it.

I knew my crime was great, and under ordinary circumstances, I would have gone down on my knees and admitted it. But just then I wasn't in a mood to accept the accusing note in Joanne's voice, and I *was* in a mood to take out my sourness on someone. So I did, and sparks flew once more, and Mom had to compose another lecture.

I don't know why I record all these shameful things when I'd rather forget them. To think that all this fuss was about such trivial matters. And I had vowed never again to let myself get into such a shape after that memorable morning almost four weeks ago.

I'm sick and tired of myself. It seems so hopeless and useless — this trying and trying to do better and seemingly getting nowhere. After all, I am nineteen years old and a schoolteacher. Why can't I show more maturity?

Later — Mom came up a few minutes ago and apologized for being so sharp with me this morning. (Funny thing is, I was going to do the same thing, as soon as I got done scribbling in here.) She then went on to explain why Dad and she didn't think it necessary to have the house in tip top shape, when our money is needed in more important areas, and when there are so many people in the world with no homes at all.

I appreciate her explaining it all to me, but she wouldn't have had to. I knew it all in my heart already, even in the middle of my arguing this morning. I admire people who try to live in a simple way. I can't imagine Anabaptist or early Christian homes looking like some Amish homes do nowadays, and I think that perhaps these fancy, spiffed-up houses are part of the world dragged into our churches. But so often I forget that I have these convictions, and start longing to keep up with the Joneses.

Dear Mom. I've been trying to imagine her as a young girl like myself. I wonder if perhaps she had some of the same struggles I have. Perhaps one of her struggles now is to have patience with her daughters. Sometimes I think she scolds too much, but who am I to judge? Hard telling what I would do if I were in her place, with a daughter like me!

December 7,

We were at church today again and heard some inspiring sermons. I wonder if the ministers realize how much encouragement and good they do by preaching God's Word to us. I feel as if someone had given me a drink of cold water.

We were reminded that the Christian's life is made

up of falling and rising again, and that the difference between a Christian and a non-Christian is not that the Christian never falls, but that he always stands up again. Whereas the non-Christian makes no effort to rise.

That's a point that has often been brought out before, but it never really soaked in like it did today.

There were a lot of other encouraging points brought out also. Ivan Eash is a talented speaker. His listeners sit there spellbound, hanging on to every word he has to say.

It has been bothering me for awhile already that I associate so much more with Ruth and Annie than I do with any of the other girls. So today after church, I bravely decided to turn over a new leaf. I wasn't sure just how or where to start until I noticed Mary Mast standing in a corner, looking miserable and lonely. I was surprised how much my talking with her seemed to cheer her up. It's a shame I haven't done more of it before.

Mary sure is different than her brother Peter. I think they might have the same underlying problem though — only they react to it in different ways. Mary is so shy and self-conscious, while Peter delights in showing off and in being a loud-mouth. I have often wondered what makes that family so different and maladjusted.

I've had some tough battles with Peter. I'm trying to understand the insecure little boy behind his defiant ways and to treat him with respect. I think he's beginning to respond. The last while he's ever so cooperative and helpful.

December 18,

Tonight we had a top family evening. David, Mary Anne and Elizabeth dropped in for supper, and after supper Steve got the notion that he wanted an old-fashioned family taffy pulling.

Both Joanne and I turned up our noses at him and said we were too lazy to go to all that bother just to please him.

"Very well. Then I'll have to make the taffy myself," he said and jumped up and rolled up his sleeves.

So Hannah dug out the cookbook, Joanne poked up the fire, and I ran upstairs to get him one of our longest and widest aprons. (It didn't half reach around him.) Mom gathered the sugar, salt, corn syrup and margarine.

Steve looked ever so funny, hustling around the kitchen, apron flapping around his pants legs, and Nathan tagging at his heels as his right hand man. Mom, Mary Anne, and we girls sat and laughed at them until Steve shooed us away with our big, brown hand towel and gave us orders to stay out of sight until he called us.

So we retreated to the living room to join Dad and David, and had a great time trying to get Elizabeth to walk. Just as we succeeded in getting her to take a few tottering steps, Steve came into the room, a crestfallen look on his face, and a sheet full of gooey brownness in his hand.

"There's something wrong with this stuff," he declared. "I've had it out in that snow at least half an hour and it doesn't get a bit harder than it was."

"Are you sure you put in enough sugar?"

"Yes."

"Corn syrup?"

"Yes."

"Gelatine?"

Steve's mouth dropped open. "Gelatine? What's gelatine? The recipe didn't ask for something like that, did it?"

Of course, it had, but evidently Steve had overlooked it, and Mom had forgotten to set it out for him. We girls had been hoping he would do something wrong anyway, so we didn't mind.

We ended up sitting around the kitchen table, eating the sticky mess with spoons while Dad read us a story from Family Life. It was a magic hour. I loved my family so much it hurt. What could be more special than this feeling of family closeness in a cheery, comfy house? (It didn't even seem homely and worn-out just then!)

Then I happened to look out the window and saw the light in the Fisher home up on the hill. I couldn't help but wonder what they were doing and thinking. Very likely they were still mourning the empty place in their family circle. Somehow, it spoiled the rest of the evening for me and I couldn't keep back a few tears.

Let me appreciate my own unbroken circle of loved ones and show it with my actions. For who knows how long we may have this blessing.

December 28,

It's hard to believe that Christmas has come and gone once again. Time goes so fast — and yet sometimes the days drag a little at school, especially the last while since I'm having trouble getting the children to live peaceably with each other. I'm not sure where it all started, but I've been aware of an undercurrent of ill feelings all along. There seem to be two sides — with two or three families against two or three others, while the rest stand at the sidelines and try to be neutral.

I hate to admit it, but I fear the fault doesn't all lie with the pupils. There seems to be some friction among the older members of the same families.

January 10,

The other day, I decided things had gone far enough at school, and I gave them a good lecture about practicing love and forgiveness among each other. So far I've been very pleased by their efforts to do better. I came home from school tonight, feeling extra happy and satisfied.

As soon as I stepped into the kitchen, I noticed Dad and Mom in a corner, talking in low, earnest tones, with sober expressions on their faces. They quit as soon as they saw me, but I'd heard enough of their conversation to make me properly curious.

Later I asked Joanne if she knew what was wrong, and she told the part of the story she knew. Ivan Eash was here most of the afternoon, talking with Dad, and she heard snatches of conversation from her station beside the sewing machine.

I don't care to record it all, not even in my journal, but evidently the friction between some of the members of the church is worse than we realized. There have been some hot words.

I don't know when I've felt so disappointed — so

let down. How can professing Christians, who have sat beneath inspiring sermons from time to time all their lives, who have daily access to the Bible and its teachings, who, only such a short time ago, gazed down upon the still, lifeless form of one of their brethren — how can they show so little love? How can they say the Lord's prayer, day after day, and not remember that if we want to be forgiven, we must forgive?

How can they be such poor examples to us young folks who are looking to them for guidance? And how can they expect their children to get along with their schoolmates, when they, who are to be mature Christians, cannot get along with their brothers and sisters in the church?

Aren't there any true, peace-loving disciples left on this earth?

Any headways we have made in school seems to have been undone. I want my pupils to grow up in peace and unity, and to learn to respect the people around them. How can they, when they have their parents' example to follow?

Maybe I have the wrong attitude and am bitter myself. But I want, want, want to be able to trust and respect my fellow church members. I want to have strong Christians to look up to. I want to be assured that it is possible to live a meek, God-fearing life even in this day and age.

But just now my confidence in mankind is almost dead.

January 11,

I feel many times better tonight, thanks to Dad

and Mom.

Dad, Mom, Joanne, Steve, and I had a good, long talk about the ill feelings in the church. I feel sorry for the children who can't talk things over with their parents. Sometimes it can make the world of difference in how I feel about something.

Dad said we dare not lose confidence in the church and people here, or grow bitter ourselves. He said the best thing we can do to better things is to pray, keep our own hearts free from ill feelings, and do all we can to heal the breach that seems to be widening so rapidly.

One thing Mom mentioned is that a good place to start cultivating good feelings and love is right here at home. I was kind of hard hit. Of course, I love my family, so much — but I don't always act as though I did.

I was bitter last night, and too pessimistic. I know there are a lot of concerned people in our church who are struggling to keep things on the right track. Thank God for them.

January 31,

Today is the last day in January, and that is hard to believe. Less than three months until Ervin and Joanne's planned wedding date on April 20.

Joanne is changing, slowly but surely, though I can't really put a finger on where and how she is different. She is more serious, perhaps — less of a girl and more of a woman. But I still can't imagine her as Joanne the wife, or perhaps someday, a mother.

And it is still a puzzle to me, how she could learn

to love Ervin enough in a mere year's time to be willing to leave her family, whom she's known and lived with all her life.

I must be made out of different stuff, because I don't think I could do it, at least not for any of the boys I have met so far.

February 6,

Today was a schoolday too interesting to let it slip by unrecorded.

There must have been something in the air that made the pupils hopelessly dense. I didn't have a single class that didn't try out my patience.

Well, by midafternoon my nerves were frazzled and worn thin. I explained fractions to the fifth graders for the third time, and was ready to call up the next class when I suddenly changed my mind. What was the use of struggling and sweating when we had given up on ourselves. Learning arithmetic was hopeless.

"Okay, students, I want everybody's attention," I announced, and waited until I had it before going on. "I've just made an on-the-spur-of-the-moment decision. I want you all to clear off your desks and get ready for a little break. We've worked hard enough for one day."

It was fun to watch the pupils' reactions as they triumphantly crammed their arithmetic books and papers into their deaks, and turned beaming faces in my direction.

"Now," I went on, "we're going to play a game we used to play when I was a little girl. Some of you might not like it very well, but if you all join in and cooperate, it's going to be fun. Do you promise to do that, or would you rather turn back to your arithmetic books?"

All hands shot into the air without hesitation (even Peter's — the school's usual killjoy) and I took it to mean that they were willing to promise.

"Good, now I'm going to begin telling you a story, and I'll keep telling it until I come to a real interesting place and then I'm going to stop and point to someone else. That person will have to go on with the story until he reaches an interesting part, and then he may stop and point to the next person. Do you all understand?"

Nods and a few groans. So after warning everybody to be sensible and to talk in loud, clear voices, I launched my story.

"Once upon a time," I began, "there was a little boy. His name was Johnny. He was not a very good little boy. His father kept saying, 'Now, Johnny, be good.' His mother said, 'Johnny, be good,' and all his brothers and sisters said, 'Johnny, do be good.' But Johnny-be-good was still a bad little boy.

"One day Johnny was feeling very sad. 'I wish I wouldn't be bad all the time,' he thought. 'I want my dad and my mom to like me. I want them to tell me that I am a good little boy.'

"He sat down and he thought and he thought. Suddenly, he jumped up and he said, 'I know what I'm going to do. I'm going to do something nice for Mom. Then he ran for the house — "

I stopped and pointed a finger at Elsie, my seventh grade genius when it comes to composing original stories.

Elsie lived up to my expectations and didn't bat an eye.

"And got out the cookbook," she went on promptly. "There was a big smile on his face. 'I'm going to bake a cake for Mother while she picks the strawberries,' he said to himself. 'That will make her happy. Then she will like me.' So he got out the cake pan and dumped in a cupful of sugar, flour, and milk. Then he got two eggs and broke them into the pan. Finally he had put in everything the recipe asked for. He didn't think the batter looked like his mother's usually did so he got a big spoon and stirred it, aaaaannnnnddddd —" Elsie pointed to Henry, who is also in grade seven.

I almost laughed at the expression on Henry's face. He scratched his head and looked blank. Then he grinned. "I know what he did. He picked it up to carry it to the stove, and his foot caught on the rug and he dumped the whole cake on the floor. and then — Peter, you go on."

Everyone gasped and snickered unsympathetically at this new misfortune of Johnny's, and turned their attention to Peter.

Peter: "His mother got very mad and spanked him hard. Then Johnny got mad too and ran away to the woods —"

Isaac: "He cried and cried and then he went to sleep under a tree."

Laura: "He woke up and was hungry so he ate some wild raspberries and cracked some hickory nuts with two stones. Then he went to sleep again."

Nathan: "Soon it was dark, but Johnny didn't know it because he was still sleeping. A snake crawled right over his foot, and a little baby fox smelled him. That made him wake up, and then he was very scared because everything was so dark and he wanted to go home. He was very cold because he was lying on the snow. Then he saw a light coming closer and closer and closer, and then —" Nathan stopped abruptly after this lengthy contribution to the story, and pointed to little Martha sitting across the aisle from him.

Martha looked terrified and very promptly burst into tears. I hastened to assure her that she didn't need to help since she was only in the first grade. I glanced at the clock, and saw that it was nearly quitting time so I decided to wind up the story. Besides I had noticed that the children were getting to be a bit giddy, and I was afraid someone would say something to spoil the success of our little story so far.

So I got little Johnny rescued from his plight, reconciled to his parents, assured that he was loved after all, and reformed to an over-all good little boy.

I had barely quit talking when Henry started waving his hand, a big smirk on his face. "Where did Johnny live?" he asked.

"I don't know. Why?"

"Is there a place where you can pick strawberries and raspberries, and then lie down on the snow to sleep?"

I don't know why that struck us so funny, but the whole school had a laughing fit. And in the middle ot it, the schoolhouse door opened and Lewis Mast stepped in. (He stopped in to pick up his children.) I thought he looked rather grim. I wonder what he thought of us. I've heard say he thinks laughing is wrong.

February 9,

Yesterday evening I ran over to borrow a poem book from Annie. She was upstairs so I went on up. I noticed right away that she wasn't herself, and I thought it looked as though she had been crying.

I asked her if something was wrong and she broke down and wept. She said it's a constant struggle not to feel bitter about everything.

"It's too hard to think of doing without Dad for the rest of our lives," she said. "We miss him so much. It's so hard on Mom that I can hardly bear it. And oh, Lois — there's Eddie, too. I'm trying to forget him, but I can't. What shall I do? I can't shut off my love for him just like that."

What could I say? How heart-rending to stand helpless in the face of such sorrow. Just talking it over seemed to do Annie good though. I stayed quite a while, because my eyes were wet too, and I didn't want to go back down until they were in better shape.

Here I was marveling at how Annie took things in stride. I feel as though I've let her down by not being more of a friend in need these past several months.

How easy it is to get involved in daily duties and cares and forget past tragedies, while in the homes of those who are suffering, the tragedy is not so soon a thing of the past.

I met Sammy in the kitchen on my way home. He only mumbled, "Good evening," but his eyes said more, or at least I thought they did. Perhaps I am borrowing trouble.

It would mean trouble if Sammy ever asked me for my friendship. It shouldn't, because he is a nice boy, however awkwardand fumbling he may be. I would have no good reason to turn him down, would I?

That is what I would like to know. Doesn't a person go by feelings at all? How is a girl to know which one, from out of a dozen, is the right one?

The idea of having Sammy as a special friend or a future husband doesn't appeal to me in the least. But then Joanne used to think she didn't care for Ervin either. If Sammy did ask me, would it be my duty to accept him even though I feel nothing more than a sisterly, neighborly interest in him?

In a way, saying no to Sammy would be almost harder than it was to turn down Joe, because I think it would hurt him more. In other words, Sammy is the loyal type who sticks to one only, while Joe seemingly can switch from one girl to the next pretty fast. And Sammy has suffered enough.

Besides, he is Annie's brother.

At the same time, I've vowed that I'd never want to get tangled up in a 'special friend' relationship unless I'm pretty sure that he is the one I want to spend the rest of my life with.

The long and the short of these ramblings is once again, I <u>couldn't</u> say yes, and I <u>couldn't</u> say no.

February 13,

Sometimes I get disgusted with myself, and my journal-writing craze. As soon as something at all extraordinary or earthshaking comes along, I'm not satisfied till it is spilled onto the patient pages of the journal.

Joanne does not like it at all, mostly because she

thinks I should tell her things instead of writing them in here where no one will ever get any good out of them. She also says it is time I start changing my habits, or my husband will have a hard time of it! I told her I'd worry about crossing that bridge when I got to it.

At least, perhaps I could switch over to a daily, sensible recording of the year's happenings, instead of all the outpourings of my strange emotions. I guess I could make an effort in that direction, though knowing myself as well as I do, I have reservations about the outcome.

February 17,

It happens to be quite late, but I have a sob story to tell before going to bed.

Aunt Alice came up to Mom on Sunday and very sympathetically asked her if I'm getting things under control at school now, or if the going's still pretty rough. Mom was puzzled, of course, and told her that I had had some trouble getting the children to get along with each other, but that as far as she knew things were going fine otherwise.

Alice then told her that they had heard my school was in bad shape and that the pupils were pretty well running wild.

Needless to say, I was not just a little indignant when I heard it — but mostly I was bewildered and hurt. Who would say something like that about our school? And why?

To make a long story short, we traced the rumor down to Lewis Mast. He and his wife have been going all over the community, telling folks that he stopped in to pick up the children one day, and the school was in an uproar. And people evidently believed it and passed it on as a choice bit of gossip. How come nearly everybody else knew about it before I did?

I was determined not to feel bad toward the ones who started this gossip or the ones who believed it, but it is a struggle, I tell you.

It has been a lesson to me in more than one way. I can sympathize a little more with people who harbor grudges and can't seem to be able to forgive each other. It is easy enough to talk about loving each other when you don't have any reason not to. But of course, I still think the only right thing for a Christian to do is to forgive and forget, and I pray that God will help me to do so.

It didn't hurt my pride to get a good blow either. When things go well, it is easy to give the credit to oneself. Perhaps I was feeling a little smug about the good order in my school. Jolts like this bring me back to my senses and help me remember that I really am not very wonderful at all — and very incapable of walking life's road alone without the help of God.

I wish I could accept criticism better. I guess if I really were humble, it would not matter so much what other people thought of me.

February 20,

I talked with Lewis Mast's wife today about this school business in hopes that it would improve feelings all around. She didn't budge a centimeter. Said we might have been laughing at something funny, but we shouldn't have been doing that either. She quoted a few Bible verses to prove her point. "Woe unto you that laugh now, for ye shall weep." and "Sorrow is better than laughter, for by the sadness of the countenance the heart is made better."

I almost asked her how she explains the verse in Proverbs, "A merry heart doeth good like medicine," and in Ecclesiastes where it says there is a time to weep and a time to laugh. But I didn't want to be impudent so I said nothing.

We had a family discussion on the subject tonight. Perhaps we are wrong, but we all agreed that laughter is a vital part of a man's life, including that of a Christian's. People without a sense of humor are usually hard to get along with, they crack up eventually, and as King Solomon said, they could be likened to dry bones.

What better release is there for tension and frustration than a good clean laugh together? Surely God had a purpose in giving mankind the gift of laughter.

Not that I don't think it can be misused or overdone. Laughter can be cruel, a mockery, or the empty cover-up of a restless heart. I wish it would be easier to know when it is time to weep and when it is time to laugh. I have often wondered how much joking and laughing belongs to a Christian life. There's such a difference in people's ideas. Some have hardly any conscience against silly talking and laughing, while folks like Lewises seem to have too much conscience. And then there are people like Ivan Eash who have a deep insight and faith, who are very serious-minded, and at the same time are known for their sense of humor.

I suppose there are two extremes and one happy medium, the same as in other areas of life. How to find that happy medium, that is the problem.

O Lord God, another day has drawn to a close, and night has come. All day long I have toiled and striven in the battlefield of life, and now I come before you, defeated and ashamed.

God, you know I wanted to be sweet, but I snarled at my loved ones.

I wanted to be humble and I was proud.

I meant to be understanding, but I turned a cold shoulder to a soul in need.

I planned to be calm, and worked myself into a frenzy.

I wanted to be upright and honest in all my dealings, and was caught in a form of deceit.

I determined to be worthy of my trust, and then I betrayed it.

I wanted to do right, and yet I did wrong.

And so I kneel before you, tonight, O God, with a soul that is weeping and cast-down. For the good that I would do, I do not, and that which I would not do, I do. Look down upon me in mercy and forgive me once again. Forgive me, O God, love me, comfort me, and teach me how to live.

February 27,

Two and a half months left of school. In a way it seems like a long time yet, and in another way it seems hardly possible that so many days have already passed.

I think I'm finally beginning to be a teacher at

heart. Once I gave myself up to the rigors and claims of a teacher's life, and quit fretting about them, I began enjoying it, at least most of the time. I'd guess that's probably true about anything you do in life, the more you put into it, the more you get out of it.

I think I will say yes to the school board if they ask me to teach again next year.

I feel rather nervous about this diary. I have a great big, "Keep Out" and a picture of a warning finger on the outside cover but I'm not assured that that will keep some people out, in fact it might only entice them the more. I'm suspicious of Joanne. She claims that since she tells me all her secrets, she has a right to read mine. She has probably done some peeping.

To tell the truth, so have I. Joanne doesn't keep a diary, but she did get a letter from Ervin once which she said I may not read. She had it spread out right inside her dresser drawer and I opened it quite innocently. Before I knew what I was doing, I was reading - and I didn't stop right away. It bothers my conscience a little. Perhaps I should confess.

March 2,

This is sort of funny. Tonight I was sitting on the bed, clipping my finger nails and staring out the window by turns, when here comes Joanne up the stairs with her dainty step, step, step. She came in, looked me over good and hard, and said sternly, "Lois, isn't there something you would like to confess to me?"

I looked blank.

"You know, something that is bothering your conscience, something about reading a letter that was meant for your sister only?"

I stared. "But how do you--" I started to say, and then I stopped and laughed. "Aha, so you've been snooping in a journal that was meant for your sister only?"

We had a good laugh about it. Joanne saw my journal lying under a pile of papers on the table and couldn't resist peeking.

Naturally, it fell open to the page I had written last, and that was what she read.

March 3,

Last night I was unwise and read a book until past midnight. (Something I very rarely do nowadays, since I'm teaching.) We got up early this morning in order to get the butchering of fifty turkeys well under way before schooltime. I left the jolly butchering gang with reluctance and trudged through the biting sleet and wind to school, with a faint pounding in my head, and an overall 'half-there' feeling.

As anyone knows that is a bad way to start a new day. I dragged through the long hours with my main desire to see the day come to an end. My headache got worse, and I longed to grab a few minutes of sleep. I tried to stay cheerful but I hardly succeeded one hundred percent.

Jerry must have had some kind of similar problem bothering him, because he was hard to get along with all day. He didn't get his work done and he was so restless that I was tempted more than once to get hold of his ears. Finally he made one monkeyshine too many, and I told him that he could stay after school.

After school, he obediently remained in his desk, and slunk down like a frightened little puppy. But I resisted the pleading look in his big, blue eyes and began my lecture.

His eyes filled with tears and a more dejected looking Jerry I've never seen. "I- I'm sorry, Teacher," he choked out. "I - I tried to be- be good."

The enormity of his misdeeds rolled away from before my eyes. I felt only pity for this poor little boy, who so early in his young life, found it hard to be 'good'. I know that the motivation behind his showing off and cut-ups is often a desperate cry for love and attention, and I certainly did not give him the understanding he needed today.

I can't help but compare Jerry with myself. How often I too, try to be 'good', and don't succeed. How often I feel like crying with Jerry, "I'm sorry, God. I wanted to be good."

Perhaps God looks down at my strugglings and failures as I looked down into Jerry's penitent face tonight—full of pity, and love, and understanding.

March 9,

We got a letter from Grandma Yoder today. She wrote that her arthritis keeps getting steadily worse. She can hardly get around anymore. At the end of her letter, she wrote, "I keep thinking how nice it would be to have an energetic young girl like Lois or Hannah to help me out."

Dad read the letter out loud, and then asked me if I would like to go. I think he was teasing. At least I hope so.

March 12,

I need advice. Perhaps getting everything down in black and white will clear my mind and help me decide what I want to do.

Yesterday, of all things, we got a letter from Uncle Crists, seconding Grandma's plea for help. Crist wrote that both Grandpa and Grandma take a lot of care, and his wife Katie doesn't think she is up to looking after all that extra work. Moreover, there is a schoolhouse just across the road from Grandpas that will need to have a teacher for next term. Would Lois come down, board at Grandpas, help them in the mornings and evenings, and teach school during the day?

Would she? That's a good question. At first I very flatly said I would not. After all, I just got done promising the school board that I would teach here next year. And I couldn't live without my family for three-fourths of a year, could I?

But the longer I think about it, the more I keep backing down. Shouldn't I take the chance to help my grandparents? Would I be shirking my duty if I didn't go?

I can't decide how I feel about it. I hate to give up my school here (though I know that Ruth would gladly take my place.) And the idea of stepping into an unfamiliar community and school, gives me the shakes.

But I'm tired of being a baby. I'm soft—have been all my life. Perhaps an experience like this would toughen me up a bit. I don't like the idea of being so dependent on my family and all that is familiar. Other people seem to be able to do things like this. Why shouldn't I?

There's an appealing touch of adventure to the whole idea. What say you, journal, I think I'm going to do it.

March 14,

I just got done sighing a big, long, drawn-out sigh. I'm not sure just what kind of sigh it was—one of relief, or regret, or excitement. Perhaps all three combined. Relief, because a decision has been reached, regret because I will be leaving so much when I leave home for over eight months, and excitement at the thought of the unknown adventures just around the curve of time.

Dad, Mom and I hashed and rehashed the whole affair, until we finally decided that this was an opportunity that should not be shoved aside.

I hope the schoolboard here won't mind too much.

I wonder how I will like staying at Grandpas. It's a shameful thing to admit, but I don't know my own grandparents very well—or Uncle Crists. We've done some visiting back and forth, of course, but never often or long enough to break through the shell of formality.

Grandpas live on the same farm they bought thirty-two years ago, only they now live in the dowdy house and Crists in the big one.

I think I'd feel at home with Uncle Crist, but I don't know about Aunt Katie. She seems rather stiff and uppity to me, but I suppose that's because I don't know her well enough. If I remember right, they have a mansion of a house, with every nook and corner in apple-pie order.

I hope I won't regret my decision. Joanne doesn't

think she can do without me that long, but I guess if she can run off on us, so can I.

April 15,

Closer, closer, closer comes the great event. Only five more days till the wedding.

Joanne walks around in Dreamland these days and doesn't seem like herself at all anymore. Her wedding dress is ready and waiting, every stitch and line perfect.

This poor old house probably wonders what is happening. At least, I'm sure it never got a going-over like this before. What a scrubbing and cleaning! We even painted the kitchen and living room walls, though I didn't coax a bit since that time a few months ago.

And Dad actually bought Mom a new stove, installed it behind her back, (one day when Mom wasn't at home.) She sure is happy with it, in spite of the fact she's always claimed the old one's good enough for her.

I don't think I've even mentioned that I am to be one of the witnesses on Thursday, with Ervin's cousin, Mark Kauffman, from ________. I've never met him, but I imagine him to be like Ervin, homely and unexciting. Hopefully, he'll be someone who has a calming effect on me. I'm nervous. I'm usually calmest at the most hair-raising times, and vice-versa, but all those people watching us (me), might make me take a fright, turn brick red, or make some drastic mistake.

April 18,

I got a substitute for my school and entered into the spirit of cleaning and getting ready here at home.

I feel all mixed up. Part of me is excited and happy for Ervin and Joanne, and the other part of me is crying because I don't want life to change. I hate these changes. In another decade or so, our whole family will likely be scattered to the four winds, and I will be either a lonely old maid, or a married woman. Neither appeals to me. I just want to be a young girl for the rest of my life, and have my family and friends all around me.

April 23,

Ho hum. This is Sunday evening. There is no singing planned for tonight, and we were done choring and eating supper by six, so that means a delicious three or four hours of doing what I choose to do. I am going to write in here for the first hour at least. Maybe longer, because I am ready for a good, long spill.

I'll come right out and make my confession first of all. Something has changed. I think it is me. Most people probably figure I'm the same girl I was a few days ago, but I am not.

I'll have to start at the beginning of the story. It began on Thursday morning, when I first saw 'him' walk into the room. ('Him' happens to be Mark Kauffman, my partner of the day.) At first glance, I didn't think he was very striking in appearance, but he had a strange way of looking nicer and nicer as the day went on.

By evening, I had to admit that I had all the symptoms- My mind was taken up with 'Mark' and nearly every time I caught him looking at me, my face turned pink. (None of the other boys can make me do that!)

Friday morning dawned with the usual 'after the wedding' clutter and mess. I had planned to stay at home and help clean up, but just before schooltime, I got the message that my substitute was sick and couldn't teach. So I went to school after all and let the ones at home struggle along without my help.

It might not be very charitable to mention it, but I had to wonder if my substitute had perhaps been sick on Tuesday and Wednesday as well. Everything was in a mixed-up jumble, and the schoolhouse looked as though it hadn't been swept since I left. With the help of a few of the school girls we got things cleaned up a little before bell time. I had the bell in my hand, ready to shake it, when I looked out the window and beheld a buggy full of visitors unloading beside the school sidewalk. And yes— there was Mark Kauffman, looking taller and more handsome than ever.

For a minute, I had a mad desire to rush out the back door and disappear. How did they (he) dare come when we were so ill-prepared for visitors?

At least the classroom was cleaner than it had been a few minutes before. With that thought to prop me up, I rang the bell and went out to give our visitors an outward welcome at least.

I got everybody seated, the pupils at their desks, and the company on the bench at the back of the room. We rose and said the Lord's Prayer together as usual. Then I got out the Bible story book and began reading aloud. It took all my concentration to keep the unnatural shakiness out of my voice. About halfway through the story, I saw from the corner of my eye several hands waving in the air.

"Yes, Elsie," I said. "Is something the matter?"

"Yes," she said. "We read that chapter on Wednesday."

"Oh," I blinked in embarrassment, laughed a little, and paged over to the next chapter.

I had barely started reading again, when I heard a faint snicker and looked up to see more hands pedaling the air.

"Yes, Peter."

"Elsie was wrong," he said in a loud voice. "The one you read first is the one we read on Tuesday. We read the one you are reading now, on Wednesday."

"Oh," I said again, and felt the red creeping all over my face.

I finally got the right portion read, and we started singing. I thought the children sang very well, though my own voice took the liberty of cracking while helping little Martha get her song started. After some introductions, I began muddling my way through the classes, conscious all the while of a pair of brown eyes at the back of the room. It was warm that morning, and all the warmth seemed to settle in my cheeks.

Finally though, my usual calm and composure gained the upper hand. After all, I did know what I was doing, though it might not look like it, and they (or he) had no business stepping in and unnerving me like that! By recess I was once more as calm and cool as ice, and had a nice, comfortable talk with the visitors before they left.

Mark was here for supper and the night (Steve had invited him and Ervin and Joanne were here) and then he and the rest of his load started back the next morning.

Since then I've been in a tumbled state of mind— upside down and down side up and in short—in one mixed up mess.

I don't believe in 'love at first sight' so this must be an infatuation of some kind. Perhaps because he seemed so much like my 'dream man'— someone like my brothers, whom I think I could respect and look up to.

I thought I wasn't the type to take such tumbles, at least not such sudden ones. How have the mighty fallen! I dare say I'll soon forget it all. I might as well, because I doubt that I will ever see him again.

April 28,

I'm feeling a trifle blue tonight, and forlorn and lonely. I miss Joanne, though life does go on without her.

I stopped in at their cozy little house tonight after school, and Joanne almost cried at the sight of me. Said she was having a lonesome spell for all of us. Of course, she claims she'd miss Ervin even more.

If I ever do get married, I hope to have a cute little house like Ervin and Joanne's. I don't like big mansions.

I know I'm being bad, but when I think of having a home of my own some day, I somehow think of Mark, too. And I must not— must not do so. I don't want to get myself into a heartache. After all, I hardly know him, and I doubt that he even noticed me much.

Evidently, I wasn't the only one impressed with him though. Steve keeps talking about him, and Ervin claims he's an outstanding young man.

April 30,

Only two more weeks of school. I can hardly begin to believe it. Of course I'm glad for a holiday. It will be a relief to act like a little, carefree girl again.

I decided that I'd like to be free in another way, too—free and single for a long time to come, unhindered by the worries and heartaches love can bring with it. What a bunch of wierdness I've written in these last few pages. My heart is almost back to its cold, usual self, I think. I'm not sure.

At least I'm not as miserable as I was. It felt as though a big hunk of my world had suddenly dropped from me into outer space when that visitor left.

May 1,

"Let me be a messenger of hope,
Let me be a messenger of peace,
Let me work where troubled waters roll,
To help the troubled waters cease."

There are troubled waters all around us. Sometimes it seems hopeless even to try to do good, because the world is so permeated with evil.

If only we could keep that evil out of our churches. I keep struggling to have confidence in some of the people here. I don't want to lose my respect for those who were my heroes ever since I've been old enough to think. But I can't keep from wondering about some things. Why can't we get along with each other? Something must be wrong somewhere. Have we lost our first love?

O God, forgive us, thy people, for we have sinned. How can we love God, and not love each other?

May 17,

The last day of the school year is gone. It was something in the future for a long time, then for a few short hours it was in the present, and then it silently and swiftly glided its way into the past.

I feel as though I had been shackled and bowed down by the heavy chains of responsibility for a long time, and now I am suddenly loosed and set free. I also feel as though I had been stripped. I feel so empty and hollow inside. Especially since I know I won't be teaching 'my' pupils next year.

There would be so much of this past school year that I would like to write down—so much of memories, of lessons learned, new insights gained—and the whole, big challenge of teaching bright-eyed, unpredictable, lovable children.

I'm still basking in the afterglow of all the smiles, kind words, and compliments I received today.

The pupils presented me with a quilt with all their names stitched on it. Quite a few of them said they wished I would teach next year.

But the crowning glory came when Lewis Betty called me aside and said she wants to talk with me a bit. She actually, really, and truly apologized for the rumor they started about my school last winter. She said someone else had talked with them about it, and said that I was getting along just fine with my school. She kept apologizing, and then for good measure, heaped on a bunch of flattery. One thing that did do me a lot of good though was when she mentioned Peter. He told them he wishes I would teach again next year. Coming from Peter, that's not flattery, it's a compliment of the highest kind.

It has been a good year. Good-bye, school worries and joys, until next fall.

I wonder what my pupils will be like next year.

May 19,

News! Another daughter was born to David and Mary Anne last night, named Hannah. Sister Hannah is as tickled as can be, though she tries to hide it. And I'm a bit jealous.

It's a relief to know that everything seems to be okay.

Too tired to write more.

May 20,

I just got done washing a huge stack of dishes. Hannah and Nathan went on a baking spree this afternoon and messed up about every bowl and spoon in the house, I believe.

I was along to town this afternoon to fetch home Mary Anne and baby Hannah, due to a well-timed dentist appointment. Mom and David also went along. I got my tooth patched up and then went shopping, and took a tour through the farmers' market. As usual it was crowded with people of every description. I was struck by the expressions on their faces. Hardened, defiant, miserable, dejected, haughty, mentally disturbed, and downright wicked, but I couldn't find a face that looked truly peaceful and happy.

We went up to the hospital after awhile. The nursery was packed with babies, and I could hardly stop looking at their tiny, innocent little faces. It was hard to imagine that once upon a time that mass of humanity at the farmers' market had been little babies as sweet and innocent as these. Or that one day, these dear little angels might have that sin-hardened glint in their eyes. I longed to gather them up and protect them from such a fate.

How can it be fair that little Hannah was singled out from those other babies, to be born to Christian parents who will do their best to give loving care to her soul as well as to her body, while many of those babies, just as dear and innocent as our Hannah, will be tainted and crippled by the influence of godless homes, with parents who puff clouds of smoke into their baby faces, fill their little ears with profanity, and give them an early start in wickedness and unrest.

Why are we given more of a chance than they?

May 23,

Got a letter from the ______________ school board today, thanking me for accepting the teaching position there, and adding a few words of information concerning the school.

I will be having twenty pupils in grades one to eight.

But I don't want to think about school now, or of leaving home. I just want to relax and be free as a bird as long as I can.

We had our first meal of strawberries tonight.

June 7,

"What is fairer than a day in June?"

What a glorious evening!

I am sitting here with my back against the old weeping willow in front of the house, just thinking and letting the sights and sounds and smells saturate me through and through. I wish I could capture and hold in my heart the peace and the life and beauty of the things I hear and see and smell.

The endless, open sky above me, half blue, half clouded over, with a great yellow ball of a sun rolling its westward way down the center.

The teasing evening breeze, blowing against my cheeks and grabbing at my hair.

The delicate perfume of some late lilacs and a few early roses tickling my nostrils and mingling with the smell of freshly mown grass.

Irises, of all shades and colors, leaning their heads against the once white picket fence bordering the garden.

The lush green grass covering our sloping lawn with its generous sprinkling of yellow dandelions.

Martins warbling—fussing, scolding, swooping, gliding, diving— over my head.

The triumphant trilling of spring peepers, rising above the murky waters of our pond.

Robins singing—

Pigeons cooing—

The pleading, creaking whisper of the windmill- "You're swe-ee-ee-e-t. You're swe-e-e-e-e-et."

The distant clip clop, clip clop of a horse's hooves beating against the pavement, growing clearer, then fading away.

The faint musical whistle of Sammy from over the hill, as his lanky figure strides to the barn.

Hannah and Nathan's laughing voices calling out by turn, "Andy Over. Pigtail."

The incessant purring of Tabby, the cat, as in utter devotion he rubs his hairy self all over me.

A wooly worm, cocking its head in a moment of sober contemplation before beginning the dangerous journey across one corner of my apron.

What a beautiful world– What peace–

And yet–how much peace is there in the world? In my heart? What is beautiful scenery and peace of nature when peace is so far removed from the hearts of men? When the whole world seems to be a boiling pot of hatred and evil and fear–all that is the opposite of happiness and peace?

Why don't I have peace in my heart tonight? Why do I keep questioning an all-wise God?

I think it began the evening we went to the hospital to bring home Hannah. I began questioning things I never really bothered to think through before.

God is a just God. Then why must little children suffer for the sins of their parents?

Somewhere in Proverbs it says if a child is trained in the way he should go, he will not depart from it when he is old. In other words, if I'm trained right, I'll likely turn out all right. If I'm not, I won't. A child can't help it if he is born into a godless home, can he? Sure, he still has the freedom to choose a Christian life, but facts remain the same— There is very little chance that he will, if he has been exposed to evil influences all his life.

Not very many things in this world seem fair to

me. Why do some people seemingly get all they want, while fate is set against others? Some people are born with beautiful faces, charming personalities, and tact. Others are ugly, with warped and unlovable ways. One person blessed with an overabundance of talents, while the next has hardly one to his name? Why can one boy get the girl of his dreams, (or vice versa) at the snap of his fingers, while the next one is turned down and disappointed again and again?

Why was Dan killed and the rest of us left? Why was Dan's family broken and ours is still complete? Why must some people suffer so much more than others?

That's just a start to the questions that have been plaguing me the last while. The other day a feed salesman stopped in and Dad told him to step inside while he took his order. Dad mentioned Dan's death and that got the salesman talking. He said he can hardly stand hearing us folks talk so meekly about it all being a part of God's plan.

"Your religion is all just hogwash," he said. "I don't believe there is a God, and if there is, he's a harsh and unfeeling one. If you'd have witnessed all the tragedies and injustices that I have witnessed, you wouldn't argue with me."

Somehow his bitterness made me feel awful. I wondered how he dared talk like that. And it made me realize all the more that I dare not doubt God's existence—or his wisdom and love.

I do believe in God, I know I do. And yet, there is that one small part of me that keeps asking questions, and longing for some clear-cut proof that will make clearer and surer the story I have heard since childhood. Something that will bring God closer, and make Him less vague and unapproachable.

There have been times, many of them, in my life, when God seemed close and real to me, but there are also far too many times when my heart feels numb and devoid of feeling, when it all seems ungraspable and hard to understand.

I am only a young girl, one among millions, searching for answers and the meaning of life. There are so many things I don't understand, so many things I don't know. Still, one thing I know, I have a great longing to draw closer to God. Lord, forgive me my unbelief, help me to believe and to trust in you with all my heart.

The sun has just sunk out of sight, leaving the western horizon painted with a breathtaking flush of color. It is the finishing touch to a perfect summer evening. Does God try to speak through beauty such as this?

June 12,

"Is God—?" "Hath God—?" "Doth God—?"
Man's "Why?" and "How?"
In ceaseless iteration storm the sky.

"I am, "I will," "I do."
Sure word of God,
Yea and Amen, Christ answereth each cry:
To all our anguished questionings and doubts
Eternal affirmation and reply."

(Annie Johnson Flint)

"For now we see through a glass, darkly, but then

face to face: now I know in part, but then I shall know even as also I am known." I Corinthians 13:13

"Ask, and it shall be given you; seek and ye shall find; knock, and it shall be opened unto you." Matthew 7:7

"Be still and know that I am God. I will be exalted among the heathen, I will be exalted in the earth." Psalms 46:10

I've thought about and reread those verses until I know them by heart. I seem to hear God talking to me through them. Surely God's promises are true, and His ways are not our ways.

June 21,

Sunday—Came home from church a while ago.

I wonder sometimes if the people I live with, and the folks I meet from day to day, are wrestling with the same problems I am. It seems all I write in my journal anymore is about my feelings and struggles, but it usually makes me feel better after I've jotted them down.

My questions have turned into a different channel. I have been trying to take a good look at myself. I am beginning to wonder if I really know the God I profess to serve. Is my Christian life something healthy and growing, or is there still too much emptiness—too much hypocrisy? Have I accepted Christianity blindly, because everybody expected me to? Has hearing all the Biblical accounts ever since my baby mind could comprehend them, deadened me to the marvel and the wonder, the beauty and reality of God's creation?

For instance, I say that I know that once upon a

time, Jesus was born of Mary, came down from heaven to die a cruel death at the hands of the Jews, to atone for the sins of the human race and to save me from being eternally lost. And yet, do I really know and realize it? Does the knowledge of it move me to the great love and gratitude I ought to feel?

I say that I know there is a heaven above us, that there is a God reigning over us who will bring the whole world to a final and terrible judgement—possibly very soon. I say that I know that even if I live to be an old woman, time is short and death is not far away. I say I know these things, and yet I go about my work all day and forget it, and get wrapped up in earthly cares until heavenly things seem remote and unfathomable. My life cycle consists too much of getting up in the morning, praying hurriedly to a God that does not seem real enough, getting caught up in the day's whirlwind of activity—and dropping back into bed at night. My little mind wanders too little from the immediate activity at hand, seldom stopping to really think, and to remember why we are on this earth, and that we are heading for eternity.

Why is it so easy to do that, when I know in my heart that nothing is more sure than death and eternity, nothing more important in all the world than a daily preparing for the life which is to come?

Oh, for a closer walk with God. Sometimes I think I am gaining ground, and then before I know what is happening, I find that Satan and the world have estranged me from my God again.

Lord, let me not grow discouraged, but daily remind me that I must never, never give up, never quit working, pressing toward my goal.

Help me to learn more of your ways. I am so far removed from your glory. Touch my life. Be real to me and let me talk with you as I talk to a dear friend.

June 22,

This morning David stopped in with the reports of a sick Elizabeth, fussy Hannah, a worn-out Mary Anne, and a bunch of peas to pick and can. Of course, Mom offered to send one of the girls to help. David was heading in the opposite direction, and none of our driving horses were available, so I decided to set out on foot.

When I passed the Fisher farm, I noticed Sammy hitching one of their horses to the buggy. The dreadful thought entered my mind that perhaps he would be heading the same direction I was and would offer me a ride.

I like Sammy too much to want to give him the chance to say in words what I think he's been trying to say with his eyes the last while. Besides, I can never decide how to act in his presence. When I'm too friendly, I'm stricken with guilt, and when I'm barely sociable, I feel guiltier yet. Some people might be able to arrive at a happy inbetween, but I can't manage it.

I began to hurry, so that if there had to be a ride, it would be a short one. A few furtive glances revealed the horse and buggy making the turn at the end of the lane and coming my way. I slowed to a walk and hoped that Sammy hadn't seen me run, or that he wouldn't guess the motive behind it.

It sure didn't take that buggy long to catch up with me. I heard Sammy's gruff, "Whoa," and then he was looking down at me.

"Good morning. Do you want a ride?"

"Oh, I guess."

Sammy looked so nervous and unsure of himself that I gave him an extra, bright smile as I climbed into the buggy. "Okay," I told myself. "That smile should be enough to show him I'm not his enemy, so now it's time to be a wet blanket."

Sammy clicked to his horse and cleared his throat. "Nice morning, isn't it?"

"Yes."

"I heard it's supposed to rain by this afternoon."

"Oh."

"Did you get all your hay in now?"

"No."

Pause.

"Where are you headed?"

"Davids."

"You mean you were going to walk all the way?"

"Yes."

"Pretty far, isn't it?"

"I really like to walk."

"Oh," Sammy looked beaten, and I felt like a heartless wretch. How downright mean of me — to say something like that after he had given me a ride. And I wouldn't have had to give him quite such short, snobby answers.

"The real reason I walked is because none of the horses were available," I said hurriedly, in an attempt to make amends. "It sure was nice to be able to get a ride anyhow. Mary Anne needs help with her canning today. Where are you going? To Davids, too?"

"No. To Emanuel Peacheys. I know it's further around this way but - ah, I happened to see you head this way, and I thought you might be glad for a ride."

"That was nice." (Now why did I give him another dazzling smile?)

For a moment silence reigned in the buggy, and then Sammy cleared his throat. It had an ominous, important ring to it that doubled the speed of my heart.

"Ah, ah, I — I —" Sammy stopped, and my heart nearly did, too. So the time had come.

"Ah, I - I was wondering if — if — ah — I mean, when will you be leaving for ___________?"

"I'm not quite sure yet," I said in a voice that sounded nearly as shaky as Sammy's had been. "Probably the last of August."

"I — ah — we're going to miss you a lot."

Still not out of danger. "I must get him off the track somehow," I thought desperately, and struggled to make my voice sound cold and indifferent as I answered. "I'll probably miss the folks at home too, especially my family."

"Uh huh."

Silence once more, and what a strained and tense silence it was. It was the longest two miles I've experienced. I stared at old Duchess' unconcerned back and willed her lazy old bones to move faster.

Our death-like silence held until we reached the end of David's lane. I wished I could apologize to the poor boy beside me for being such a hopeless mixture of a snob and a flirt, for making it so hard for him to say what I'm almost sure he wanted to say, and for being seemingly unable to give him what he wanted.

But of course, I didn't dare say anything. I only jumped off the buggy, smiled my thanks from the safety of the ground, and hurried to David's house.

It took a while to get my nerves back to their normal state, and I suppose Mary Anne wondered what was wrong with me.

Poor Sammy. I'm almost sure he would have asked me for a date or something, if I hadn't snubbed him. I was so distraught at the moment and felt so sorry for him that I probably would have said yes.

Perhaps that would have been the best thing to do. Sammy needs a friend, if anyone does, someone to give him encouragement and self-assurance, especially since his father died and the responsibility of the farm managing lies on his young shoulders.

I still can't forget that look in his blue eyes, and the way his voice and hands shook. Oh, journal, I can't bear the thought of being so mean. I want to make Sammy happy, so much, but would that really be making him happy by accepting him out of pity alone? Can I force myself to have the right feeling for him?

If that Mark had never stepped briefly into my life, I might be more willing to try it. Why does the memory of him stick to my brains and heart like a cockle burr? How ridiculous to let a stranger have a bigger place in my heart than an old school friend and lifelong acquaintance.

July 16,

It's pouring great drops of rain, the rain that Sammy predicted the other day already, I guess.

We got the hay all in just in time! We've been working hard at it from dawn to dusk all week. I'm in my glory when I can do that kind of work, although Mom keeps worrying that I'll overdo myself. I guess I should have been a boy.

Sometimes I nearly wish I could either be a boy or a real lady. Joanne and Hannah would never be tempted to do the tomboyish things I would like to do.

And my big hands and feet and stocky figure — I wonder how it would seem to be small-featured and cute.

I guess I'm a French work horse, as Laura Ingalls called herself in one of her Prairie books. And if that is what I was created to be, I guess I shall be satisfied with it.

Davids are here. Hannah I (as Steve calls her) came up just now and deposited Hannah II in my lap. Hannah II is getting big and fat and will soon catch up with Elizabeth at the rate she is growing. Elizabeth has much tinier features.

Elizabeth also came upstairs and is crawling all over me and lisping, "Loli (Lois) this and Loli that." Nieces sure are fun.

July 20,

Could I learn the art of organization and neatness, I wonder, or is it something as unobtainable for me as being small-featured and petite? Mom has her definite opinions about the matter. She is quite sure that I could if I really tried. Mamas are usually right, but I stick to the belief that I was born disoriented and disorganized. I'm not saying that I couldn't possibly overcome those bad habits, but I do say that it would be a lot harder for me than for Mom or Joanne. They were born as neat as pins.

I blame no one for blaming me, because I am quite aggravating. When I clean up, I rush around putting things away and am barely done when a deluge of indignant questions rain on my defenseless head. "Lois, did you do something with my cap?" "Where did you put my shoes?" "What happened to the check that was lying on the desk?" "Lois, I want my hair pins, right now."

And poor me, I don't have the slightest idea in which drawer or cubby hole I put all those things, or indeed that I did anything with them at all.

And I leave the cake in the oven to be burned to a black crisp and a billowing stench. I forget to close my window and in so doing, grant admittance to hordes of buzzing flies. I forget to turn off the water tap in the horse stable and flood that part of the barn. And I forget this and forget that, until I have earned myself a very sad reputation.

Mom can't understand why I don't take care of things, or see the need to keep my mind on my work. But that's not the problem. I do see the need. I understand full well that it makes no sense to write long, newsy letters and then lose them, just because I don't put them in the mailbox or in a safe place. I know it's pointless to borrow patterns, and then lose them before I get around to using them.

It is all very discouraging. Ever since I can remember I have been battling with stockings. Every time I get a new pair, I resolve very firmly that I'm going to keep them (both of them) for a long time. After all, what should be hard about remembering to stick them into my Sunday shoes every time I take them off? Simple as it may sound, the only reward for my valiant efforts is a drawer full of single, unmatched stockings. Always only one stocking makes its escape. Where it goes to and how, remains one of life's mysteries to me.

Maybe the problem with me is that I've lost all faith in an actual reformation of my ways. I try, but half-heartedly, because I know that after a while I'll be right back in my old rut anyhow.

Mom worries about sending me to Grandpa's house, and at the same time I suspect that she is secretly hoping that Grandma's exacting, orderly ways will do me good.

I'm sure that I worry about it even more than Mom does. I'm beginning to get a sinking feeling whenever I think of the up-coming schoolterm. It looms ever nearer and greater in the future like a formidable mountain.

It's actually not the teaching of school itself that scares me as much as the idea of leaving home and placing myself in a wilderness of strangers.

I keep trying to imagine what my new pupils will be like. Since children are universally the same, I suppose there will be Peters and Jerrys to try me out and be my black sheep, an Ellen or two to be my gray sheep, and hopefully, some little Marthas and Marys and Elsies to be my teacher's joys.

August 1,

Yesterday I went home with Mary Miller after church. She has been asking me to for a long time. We walked back to the woods, and somehow Mary really got started talking. She told me all kinds of things about their family problems, and about the struggles she has. She told me over and over how I have helped her in the past few months, and how thankful she is for a friend like me. It made me feel good to think that I might have added some cheer and meaning to her life.

August 19,

The hands of the alarm clock on my night stand are pointing to 2:57 right now, this early Tuesday morning, August the nineteenth, 19__. In two hours and three minutes, I should be leaving for Grandpa's, if nothing happens. I am tempted to wish something would happen, to cancel my obligation to be Shady Rill's teacher.

I sure wonder what is wrong with my stomach. Something's out of order somehow. I feel even worse than I did a year ago when I began my first day at Sunnyside.

Yesterday evening as I was walking out to the barn in my chore clothes, I suddenly realized that this was the last time, for a long while, that I would go walking down that path. I milked all my favorite cows, washed the milk pails, and then ran out to the pond. I sat down on the grassy slope and pretended to be watching the ducks and geese, but my real mission was to do at least some of my crying out there, where no one could see me.

I would dearly love to wake up and find this all a dream to be laughed at and forgotten. I am scared in the true sense of the word.

There is one thing that gives me a measure of comfort though I don't really know why it should. The other day Joanne asked me very teasingly if I knew that Mark Kauffman was going to be working for one of his uncles there in __________ a few months this winter? (Not in the same district I will be in). Rather coincidental, especially since I finally had myself convinced that I had forgotten him.

Yesterday evening the whole Fisher family came over to say good-bye to me, including Sammy of course. It was rather awkward, and hard to know how to act.

I surely will miss Annie. If she would be going with me, it wouldn't be nearly so hard.

I'm going to miss Annie's mom, too. There has always been a special little friendship between the two of us. I'm not vain, but I'm almost sure that she has her heart set on me as a future daughter-in-law.

I should quit my foolish writing and see if I can get one more wink of sleep before the alarm clock sounds its noisy battle cry.

Another thing that gives me comfort is the fact that I may take my good old, familiar, black journal with me. I wonder if I would survive if I couldn't write.

The next time I open you, journal, I'll probably be many miles from home.

Greetings from Grandpa's house.

Well, I'm here. It is hardly believable that only this morning I was scribbling in these pages at

Home, sitting on my own bed, with my family's snores in my ears.

Right now I am in a house that seems deathly quiet, except for an occasional faint squeak from Grandpa's rocking chair downstairs. Grandma is in bed already.

I'm up here in what is to be my room for the next eight and a half months. It is a nice room with light blue walls and a hardwood floor, an oldfashioned mahogany bed and furniture to match, but for all that, it seems rather cold and heartless. Not the friendly type of little room I feel at home in.

I have a splendid view from my window, though. Uncle Crists' farm buildings lie sprawled in front of me. (Grandpa's house is built on a slight ridge.) If I crane my neck far enough, I can see the school house to the far right, on the other side of the blacktop road. It is situated at the very outskirts of a woods and looks very quaint and spooky with its white siding and rusty red roof half-hidden by the towering maples sprinkled here and there in the school yard.

I haven't been over to see it close-up, because we only arrived this noon, and this afternoon was spent in unpacking and poking around and visiting.

This noon when we arrived, I was hustled over to Crists for dinner. Grandpa and Grandma were there too.

It was a dinner to be remembered. Grandma sat beside me and kept urging me to eat more, so to please her I choked down a bigger meal than I've eaten in a long time. (If she keeps doing that, I dread to think what will happen to my waist line in the coming months.)

I felt like a lost puppy, taken in by strangers who meant to be kind but didn't know just exactly what to do to please me. We were all slightly uncomfortable, or at least I was.

I formed some opinions about Crist's family, and will give them to you, diary, for safe keeping.

Crist reminds me a wee bit of Dad, though he doesn't seem to have much confidence in himself, and keeps looking worriedly at his wife for approval whenever he says something. I think we are going to like each other. His most redeeming point of course, is simply the fact that he is my dad's very own brother.

I wish I could say as much about his wife, but the mere thought of her makes me sigh a long, worried sigh. I'm afraid of her. There is something about her tall thin frame, straight black hair, sharp eyes and loud, highpitched voice that makes me quake in my shoes. I get the impression it will be wise for me to walk in a pretty straight line.

I gather that she is a perfectionist—from the soles of her shining shoes to the top of her stiffly-starched cap. Her house glistens and glitters with fresh paint and the latest conveniences. I'm afraid I'll never feel at home in that house.

Katharine is the oldest of their three children. She is thirteen and will be one of my eighth graders. I haven't had time to figure her out completely, but she looks like a young lady with a will of her own. I hope I can thaw out her stiffness.

Kevin Lee is already my pet. He reminds me so much of Nathan, though he is a little older and bigger. He was rather quiet and shy today, but he flashed me several smiles that warmed my heart.

Five-year-old Carolyn is cute, with her father's blue eyes and blond hair. It took her about an hour to thaw out and then she was chattering like a magpie and climbing into my lap. My sixth sense told me that she might just be a trifle spoiled.

Grandpa and Grandma are just the same Grandpa and Grandma they have always been. I wonder how it will seem to live with them so long.

Everything is strange and unhomelike around here, but I think I've done quite well in keeping up my spirits so far. I resolved this morning on the way here, that since there was no way out of the next eight or nine months, I was going to face them with a positive outlook and make the very most of them.

August 22,

Behold, the end of my fourth day away from home. I hope I am not stretching too much when I say that it seems more like four years.

I spent the last three days over at the schoolhouse getting things lined up for Monday. That schoolhouse is spooky, and it feels haunted when I'm over there all alone. Everything about it is old-fashioned except a set of newfangled desks that contrast ridiculously. There is a peculiar musty smell in the air, though the whole building has been scrubbed and cleaned recently.

I wish Monday would come, for several reasons. I'd like to meet my pupils. It's scary business, not knowing a whit about them. (Please, please, don't let them all be as snobbish and uppity as cousin Katharine.)

And I need something to occupy my mind and get it away from home and my longing to be there. Surely time won't drag as much once school starts.

Grandma calling-

August 25,

It's no use, I've tried, I really did, but I can't stick to the positive side of life here at ________, when there is no such side.

The truth is, I'm sick with worry and dread and regret. Oh, why did I take such a step? I'm desperately homesick for my family already. Nothing seems worth living for, here. Especially today it seems that way. Even the weather is in accord with my mood. It has been raining off and on all day and the sun hasn't peeped through once.

The reason I'm extra blue is because I've been to church. It was worse than I imagined. No one was deliberately unkind, but well—it is hard to explain even in my journal.

I hadn't realized that there would be such a difference in our way of dressing and style of living in general. I've heard of girls feeling like old-fashioned mommies, but I never fully knew what they meant until today. The girls here wear short, tight dresses and small caps, with their hair hanging down over their eyebrows. They've got the most sophisticated airs and they walk through a room as though they were treading on a cloud.

This forenoon in the middle of church services, I happened to notice the striking contrast between my pair of hands, and the hands of the girls on either side of me. Mine are naturally wide and they are brown and calloused by the summer's sun and hard work. My finger nails are short and uneven. _Their_ hands were snow white and slender, with long, pointed fingernails. My first impulse was to try and get mine out of sight, but then I folded them serenely on my lap again. Mine are the hands of a farm girl, and as far as I know I need not be ashamed of them.

I don't think those girls and I have anything in common. After church they talked about their cleaning jobs in town, their latest dates, about their new dresses, and the type of material they like the best. I was lost.

Their reaction to me hurt too. Most of them tried to be friendly in their own way, but my mind-reading instinct told me plainly that they thought I was a little odd, and that they dreaded the thought of having me imposing on their jolly circle. Of course, it probably was partly my own fault. I might have appeared slightly stuck-up, but I simply didn't have the heart to go the second or third mile to be friendly to a bunch of girls with whom I wasn't in the least a kindred spirit. I have too much pride to force myself into a circle that would rather have me outside.

I didn't want to go to the singing tonight, but I still expected someone to offer to take me along, or to coax me to go. No one did.

What wonderful friends I have back home. I've never appreciated their worth half enough.

Right now, I can imagine the young folks gathered around the table in the Fishers' long, narrow livingroom, singing heartily. I can see them all—in my mind's eye, looking delightfully dear and familiar, especially Annie, Ruth, Mary, Steve, (I can just imagine him looking handsome and dressed up in his Sunday suit) and Sammy.

And somewhere, in that faithful old house on the next hill are Dad and Mom and Hannah and Nathan- and perhaps Davids and Ervins. They often come home on Sundays.

I wonder if they are thinking of me— The very thought that perhaps they are— perhaps sending a prayer upward for their homesick loved one, that is comforting. I've a feeling I'm going to need all the prayers I can get in the days to come.

Today I also saw most of my school children. I was impressed by some of them, but not favorably. I was standing against the kitchen wall when I became aware of a group of little boys in the doorway, pointing and staring in my direction. When they saw that they had gotten my attention, one of them stuck out his tongue and the others laughed, uproariously.

Is there any wonder that I am feeling the bluest kind of blue?

Those boys my future pupils? All my teaching ambition, confidence, and remaining optimism were shattered to dust at that moment. I dare not begin teaching tomorrow morning with those vital parts missing, but how can I regain them, when everything seems against me?

I did make a friend today— though not among the girls. This morning one of the women impressed me by her more conservative way of dressing, and by the look on her face. I can't really describe her expression— something of meekness and serenity, (and at the same time, kind of sad.) It must have been her inward beauty, shining through.

After church she came over to where I stood and introduced herself as Polly, wife of Melvin Glick. She mentioned that there have been some problems at Shady Rill School in the past years, and that they would be thinking of me, and do what they could to help me out.

I don't think it is fair that Uncle Crist didn't tell me about those problems when he asked me to take the job.

If Melvin Glicks' children are anything like their mother, they should be okay, at least.

I must finish my letter home.

August 26,

Dear God,

This morning, I seem to have no words with which to come before you. And yet I don't need to have, for you know it all— You know about this darkness in my heart— this dread and shrinking from the battlefield I must step onto in a few more hours. Oh Lord, I cannot do it, I cannot. I am too small, too unsure of myself. The challenge is too great. I want to crawl back into bed and hide myself under the covers.

"All things are possible through Christ which strengtheneth me." Lord, help me to hang on to that verse and believe in it with all my heart. I must believe in it, or give up before I start.

Courage, courage. Strength, faith, hope, peace. Give me these gifts, oh Lord, I cry. Guide me and keep me in the hollow of thy hand.

August 28,

Today I received two letters from home! One from

"I could hardly contain myself when I saw them lying on the windowsill."

my family and one from Annie. I could hardly contain myself when I saw them lying on the windowsill as I came home from school. It has been a long time since I felt like that.

I've read them through exactly five times now, and shall probably keep it up until I can recite them all by heart. Everyone of them wrote — even David and Mary Anne and Ervin and Joanne and Dad and Steve and Nathan. Elizabeth made some pictures and Hannah II scribbled around a bit. It was a feast for my hungry heart.

Annie writes like she talks. Full of interesting little pieces of news in an encouraging, cheerful way.

I won't begin writing about school. I wouldn't get done once I started and I am overcome with fatigue at the moment.

Only two more days of this school week. Blessed thought!

August 30,

Even the longest week can come to an end. Does that mean that this school year will also come to an end someday?

In a way I wish I could have recorded the whole of this one week's struggles, and minute-to-minute happenings, but on the other hand, I would be only too glad to be able to put it all behind me — a week forgotten, or one that never happened at all.

I am, oh, so thankful that the week did end on the upswing. For awhile I thought it would get worse every day. Even so, I can see that unless some miracle or change takes place, it will be one difficult battle—one that will take every ounce of effort that I can muster. What I am afraid of is that it will take more than I've got.

"All things are possible through Christ, which strengtheneth me."

September 1,

Dear Loved Ones at Home, from Dad to Baby Hannah,

Hello, all you dears!

I'm sitting down here in Grandpas' living room, beside the old desk that Grandma said you used to have up in your room, Dad. The place is deserted, except for Grandma and me. This morning Grandma's arthritis was bothering her quite a bit, so I offered to stay at home with her. Crist's whole family and Grandpa went over to the West district for church. I wasn't in the mood to look at and be looked at by another 200 strangers.

Grandma's sleeping out here on the couch. Is it ever quiet in here! The only sounds I can hear at the moment are the tick tock, tick tock of the clock on the wall, and an occasional snore from Grandma. This eerie stillness is something I find hard to get used to, after having lived with such a noisy family for over nineteen years. Of course, I'm exposed to more than my heart's content of noise over at the schoolhouse.

Knowing me as well as you do, I suppose you are prepared to listen to a few pages of my sad woes—how many hankies I've soaked up since leaving home, and all about my homesickness and loneliness. I will admit that it has been sort of tough, but I'm not going to waste any paper going into detail.

I am more or less settled, and getting used to the routine of life here. Get up in the morning—make breakfast for Grandpas and me, pack my lunch, walk across the road to school, spend the day there, walk back at about five, do odd jobs, make supper, eat, and spend the rest of the evening reading, writing, or working on school projects.

To be sure, eating supper doesn't leave too much room for anything else. I dare say I'm learning some much-needed patience, by sitting at the table with Grandpa and Grandma, nibbling a bit here and there, while they chew and chew, and talk and talk, and swallow pills and herbs and all kinds of home remedies. And Grandma is even worse than you are, Mom, for trying to stuff me with more food than I want or need.

And Mom, quit worrying about your reckless, impulsive daughter tearing around in Grandma's immaculate kitchen. I've been reformed to a lady as deliberate and careful as you please. I have broken no eggs or dishes, burnt no cake, misfollowed no directions, or forgotten anything of great importance— so far. But I might be tempting fate to say so.

I have seen very little of Uncle Crists. It would do me a lot of good to help them chore, but I haven't got the chance yet.

You all asked the same question, "How's school going?" To tell the truth, I'd rather wait to answer that question until I can give you a more cheerful answer. In other words, once I've got things in better order and organized more to my liking. You must remember, we've been in session for only one week.

I will say this much. One week has been long enough to reveal to me that I have quite some characters in the group. I think I will have to tell you about some of the more imposing ones.

I have three eighth grade girls (no boys), Loretta Sue Miller, Anna Marie Glick, and cousin Katharine.

Loretta Sue would be a very pretty girl, if she did not think so herself, and if she were minus her perpetual pout and her arrogant, know-it-all ways. She is the youngest in the family, I learned, which did not surprise me in the least. I am afraid that I have a very spoiled, immature young lady on my hands who would gladly rule the place as queen supreme.

Anna Marie is much quieter and meeker, but both she and Katharine are ardent followers of Loretta Sue.

I have two seventh grade boys, (no girls). Arthur is tall and broad-shouldered and looks like a young man. He has been very quiet and withdrawn so far, but I can sense that he has a mind of his own, and I'm a little afraid of him.

Arthur's shadow, Rob, verily does look like his shadow, very short and skinny. As Loretta Sue is a heroine in Anna Marie and Katharine's eyes, so Arthur is Rob's hero. Rob seems to be another of these people who is trying to hide his insecurity behind a bold front.

And then there are the Helmuth sisters, Becky and Sarah, who seem to be afraid to move for fear they will do something wrong, and— and—Benny Glick (Anna Marie and Arthur's younger brother). He's beyond anything I've ever met . He makes me laugh and cry at the same time. He could get a job at a circus as a clown with one twist of his face. In five days I've seen him screw up his face in about fifty astonishing and grotesque shapes. At hearing a shocking piece of news, he dramatically lays his hand across his heart, stares wildly for a few seconds, emits a piercing shriek, throws up his hands, and crumples slowly to the ground in an apparent dead faint.

The other day the rest of the boys rose to the occasion and solemnly picked up the limp Benny and carried him to a make-believe hospital outside. A few minutes later, imagine my horror at seeing the resurrected Benny clinging to the swaying topmost branch of a giant maple in the schoolyard. I was shaking by the time that young whippersnapper was back on safe ground once more. I gave them something of a lecture and strictly prohibited any more tree climbing on school premises.

I hope you're not tired of my rambling, because I would like to introduce you to one more little boy, first grader Ephraim. He is very small for his age and behaves in a manner as dignified as the sound of his name. He is generally as quiet as a mouse and caused no ripples in this ripple-filled school until Thursday morning when he came walking up to my desk, proudly carrying a brand-new, red-tipped scissors in his one hand. He was so very proud of that scissors and even tried to bring it with him when I called him up for classes.

Well, after recess, I was answering hands and came upon Ephraim in the act of painstakingly snipping off the curls of the unsuspecting little lass in front of him.

As soberly as I could I explained a few things to the young barber, and as a punishment temporarily took from him his beloved scissors.

Believe it or not- the next afternoon here comes Ephraim walking up to class, as dignified and composed as ever, with a big square piece of material cut out of the front of his shirt. I stared— until I found enough voice to ask, "Ephraim, what happened to your shirt?"

"My shirt?" That little brat actually had the nerve to look perplexed.

"Yes," I said and pointed to the missing part of him. (I should have pointed to his head, I think!) "What happened there?"

"Oh," said he innocently. "My new scissors did that this morning."

Please wish me the patience of Job, the wisdom of Solomon and the faith of Abraham. I will be needing endless supplies, I fear.

I wouldn't mind having someone's advice. How much should I let those pranksters get away with? They are so utterly different from my unimaginative model children at Sunnyside.

I just finished the letter home and put it in an envelope. Since the pages of this journal are the same size as my writing sheets, I decided to make a carbon copy of my letter in my diary.

I reread it just now, to make sure that it sounds cheerful enough to send. Somehow I can't bring myself to let them know how bad things really are. And though it isn't a completely rosy letter, I think it sounds reasonably cheerful and not nearly as down-hearted as I felt all week. I didn't tell them about the rebellion and tension that lie heavily in the air, or how willful Loretta Sue really is, or how much like an iceberg Katharine's attitude is toward me, or how dislikable and smart-alecky Rob is, or about the gleam of defiance in Arthur's eyes— and how wide the Jericho's wall that lies between us.

I was shocked and let-down on Monday morning, to learn that the little boy who showed me his tongue on Sunday was Benny, and that Benny is the child of Melvin and Polly Glick, as are Arthur and Anna Marie. It is hard to believe.

Crists and Grandpa will probably be coming home soon.

I wonder if Mark Kauffman is in the community.

I feel almost unbearably lonely just now, as though I had to talk to someone— someone who understands me. I hardly see Crists and though Grandpa and Grandma are so very nice to me, I can't really talk to them about the things bothering me. They are too old, and I am too young to be able to really understand each other.

September 3,

This is a Tuesday evening. In spite of a nagging cold, I feel quite refreshed, as though I had been wandering in a desert for a long time, and just stumbled onto an oasis.

Just think of it! I've found her, actually found her— a kindred spirit. Someone who actually likes me, who shares at least some of my ideas and ideals, and doesn't look at me as though I were a queer being from Mars.

Soon after school was dismissed this afternoon, a buggy drove into the school lane, a girl hopped off, tied her horse, and came walking in. (Walking— not mincing!) I knew right away that I hadn't seen her before. When I met her at the door, we smiled, shook hands, and the kindred spirits within us hailed each other.

I don't know what it was about her that made me know almost at first sight that here was the friend I was needing, someone sympathetic and sincere. I thought I could just read the warmth and depth and common sense in her face.

Anyhow, I found out in the next hour that her name is Helen Coblentz and that she's only a couple months older than I am. She lives about three miles from here, and came all this way just to meet me. She is in our church district, but wasn't there the other Sunday, because she had gone over to one of the other districts.

I suppose it sounds silly to be telling one's troubles to an 'almost' stranger but I did tell Helen some of mine. And I feel better than I have for a long time. I've even found new strength and will for the tomorrows before me.

Thank you, God, for sending me a friend. Thank you, too, for being the one friend I can always depend on when earthly friends fail. Let me never stray from you, or quit leaning on you for strength.

September 26,

I know it has been a long time since I have written in here. Three whole weeks and a half. At home that wouldn't have been long, but here I need some kind of release for my tumbled emotions.

But somehow, the last several weeks I could hardly find the will power to write letters home, much less keep up my record in here.

I'm almost worried about myself. I don't feel like the same Lois anymore. I used to be full of life and sparkle and fun. Now I feel like a wrung-out rag, with all the life squeezed out of me. I'm so tired all the time. I drop to bed as soon as I can in the evening, and in the morning I must literally force myself to get out of bed and face another day. Each morning I whisper to myself, "Heroism consists of hanging on one day longer."

I can hardly eat. This morning I stepped on the scales in Grandpas' bedroom and got a shock. I've lost over fifteen pounds since I'm here. I guess losing weight always was my dream.

I don't know how much longer I can hold out. I never dreamt there could be such a difference in schools— in children. I have always carried the idea in my head that the difference between a good school and a problem school depended pretty well on the teacher. Maybe it does. Maybe I'm not worth anything as a teacher, and my good year back home was merely chance— beginner's luck. If I ever had battles with inferiority, it's now. I feel like a failure all the way through.

All my life I've been used to being liked and loved and praised and smiled at. Somehow I was sure that I could win the love and respect of my pupils here, too. I can't. And the fact that I'm so little used to criticism and ridicule makes every dig and show of defiance hurt and smart all the more.

Back home there was an atmosphere of working together, and comradeship. I enjoyed the feeling of being admired and adored as a big sister and friend. Here, the teacher is an undisputed enemy— someone to defy. The more disrespectful and openly rebellious you dare to be, the greater your place of rank among your peers.

Sure, back home I had a Peter and a Jerry too, but they were in the minority. The school here seems to be made up of Peters and Jerrys, many times worse than my own dear Peter and Jerry at home, and the 'good' pupils are in the minority. The result of course is a constant battle of teacher versus pupils, one person against nineteen.

But the real battle is in my heart. Perhaps if I could win that battle the school battle would not seem so hopeless.

The last while it seems as though even God has turned against me, that even He is displeased with me. I've lost the heart to pray, and I keep fighting little twinges of rebellion and doubt in my heart. Why did He let this happen to me? Why doesn't He come to my aid? Didn't I pray earnestly, humbly, for his help? Won't there be any recompense for this slaving— this super-human effort day after day?

I keep thinking back longingly to my pupils of last year, and remembering that I could be there right now, basking in the sunshine of Sunnyside, instead of shivering in the shadows of Shady Rill.

I know I must stop thinking such thoughts. I am letting bitterness and rebellion poison my thinking. I am not giving my pupils and the people here a fair chance, if I compare them with the ones at home. But how can I change my outlook? I keep asking God to put love in my heart for the pupils here, but there is none there. My heart feels only empty and cold and angry at them all. I would like to shake them good and hard, and say to them, "Okay, if you don't want me I'll go back to my own children. They know how to behave and they are thoughtful and obedient, the way all children should be."

I must have love, endless supplies of love, before I can hope to win this school. I must have a dauntless faith in a God who still loves me and who is never too late with His assistance. And I must regain the faith I lost in myself.

How?

Perhaps I will find comfort by reading a chapter in my Testament.

If only Dad or Mom or Joanne were here. Perhaps they could tell me what to do.

October 2,

Dear Journal,

Hi there! This is me again, with some of my old bounce and spark regained. I had an awfully low spell for a while there, but school is going some better. I've had a few more good talks with Helen, and made friends with some of the 'stuck-up' girls.

And — ah, I guess I also did see Mark. He was in our church district last Sunday. I spotted him first thing when we drove into the lane that morning. As usual, my strange heart took a few little jumps and my stomach somersaulted. And as usual I was disgusted with myself, gave myself a mental shaking up and a sound scolding.

He was at the singing, too. I behaved myself very well and didn't even give myself the satisfaction of looking to see whether he noticed me or not. But I did find out one thing — I have not forgotten him as I thought I had for awhile there.

I've just thought of something. It is not a very happy thought, though it should be if I have any unselfishness in me. Mark and Helen would make a very nice couple. I don't see how Mark could help from seeing what a jewel she is, and vice versa.

If that is the way things will turn out, I'd better start preparing myself right away, because I am already in too deep for comfort.

I think I'll go to bed early after all. I'm tired all of a sudden.

October 10,

Ugh.

I wish I could run off to some quiet, uneventful corner of the world where there is no such thing as indecision.

It has happened this time, and pushed the question I've been dreading right under my nose.

Tonight I found a letter waiting for me on the window sill. I took one glance at it, and was taken back half a dozen years to the familiar schoolroom at Sunnyside, and to a lanky figure hunched over the desk in front of me, scribbling laboriously across the page. I recognized Sammy's peculiar stilted handwriting at once.

I took it upstairs and sat on the bed, just holding it and thinking for at least ten minutes. I didn't need to open it to know what it contained. When I finally did, I took out a lovely birthday card and a short letter, ending with these words:

> "I know I am not worthy to be asking you this question, (though I've been wanting to for a long time) but I was wondering if you would care for my friendship.
>
> I pray that God may bless you and your work.
>
> Your unworthy friend,
> Samuel Fisher"

Memory after memory came flooding to my mind. Bashful, fumbling Sammy, often nervous and unsure of himself — always a part of my life. I think I know him nearly as well as I know my brothers.

So that is that. For awhile school worries will be pushed aside, while this new battle of "shall I or shall I not?" is being fought.

Yes or no? Yes or no? Yes is too final and no is too final and maybe will only prolong the pain for both of us.

I want to say yes, because I am lonely and I know that Sammy is lonely, and because it gives me a warm feeling to know that he still cares for me. I want to say yes, because I can imagine Sammy waiting, wondering what my answer will be. I can see him opening my letter, his hands shaking, like they did that day in the buggy. I can see the look of quiet pain and disappointment in his blue eyes if the answer is no, or the light of glad surprise if it is yes. I can picture him breaking the good news to his mother and Annie with that happy, self-conscious grin on his face — and Annie nearly dancing with delight.

I would like to say yes because a woman's love would do wonders for a boy like Sammy.

Just maybe, Sammy, my answer will be — yes.

October 11,

Do I, or do I not??
The question stares me in the face.
Should I, or should I not?
<u>Should</u> I, or should I <u>not</u>?
The question stares me in the face.

For all my life lies hanging to the word
I give in answer to that question
And no one on earth can tell me,
Exactly what to do.
No one can tell me
Just what my answer ought to be.
And neither do I know.

And so I stand,
Between two forces pulling me
One whispers no,
The other, yes.

How can I know which voice is right?
Whose voice is whose?
Which voice is good —
Which comes from God
And which is voicing my self-will?
Just now I do not know.

Just now I am not sure —
But God, you know —
The only one who knows
Exactly where my future lies.

Let me be still and know that you are God,
Let me be still,
And know that you will show
Your poor weak handmaid
The answer to her quest.

October 12,

A letter, a letter, a letter from home!

And, oh joy! Dad and Mom and Ervin and Joanne are going to come visit me, really and truly. I don't think I've got my two feet on the ground anymore. I don't think Grandpas knew I could laugh and act as light-hearted as I've been acting since I read that blessed piece of news when I got home from school.

If plans hold out they'll be coming on Friday afternoon, arriving at the bus station at two o'clock sharp. And I'm going to dismiss school early and go get them.

It'll be such a lightening of my burdens to tell them all about my 'Sammy' troubles and ask them for advice. I know though, that they'll say such a decision is up to me. I wish they could just tell me what to do, and I would only need to obey. I hate needing to make up my own mind.

There is a small thought that keeps wet-blanketing the joy of having part of my family come visit me. They will likely visit school and I don't want them to. So far I have cringed at letting them find out the bare, unhappy truth — that I'm having problems, not just minor ones, but serious ones. I know they have confidence in me and I can't bear to see it shaken.

And if they visit school — well, I just don't know. Things might go all right and they might not. Those pupils are unpredictable.

October 13,

Well, journal, I've been writing in here every night, the last four evenings. I really ought to catch up on my sleep, but I'm too excited at the prospect of seeing my family tomorrow, to drop to sleep without first expending some of my energy.

And I really should tell you about the visitor I had tonight at the schoolhouse.

Today was a super-trying day, and as soon as the last of my noisy pupils were safely trotting down the road to their homes, I was overcome with my 'wrung-out rag' feeling. So I merely frowned at the harum-scarum schoolhouse and the towering stack of checking on my desk, and nestled my head in my arms for a refreshing five minute snooze.

Can you imagine, journal, there I was, dreaming sweet dreams of meeting the others at the bus station when something woke me up. I kept my head down for another minute, trying to get my drugged, still half-dreaming thoughts back to reality, when a small noise from the entrance made me jerk up my head and stare in that direction.

There was Mark Kauffman — standing in the doorway!

I gave a startled little gasp in spite of my efforts

"My disorderly schoolhouse, and the fact that he had caught me sleeping, made me wish for an empty desk drawer to crawl into."

not to. That gasp, my disorderly schoolhouse, and the fact that he had caught me sleeping, made me wish for an empty desk drawer to crawl into.

And of course, I had to blush to what must have been a deep poppy red. (He must think all I can do is blush.)

Poor Mark looked embarrassed, too (and perhaps a bit amused) but he managed to tell me what he wanted. There is to be a barn raising at Harvey Kauffmans the day after tomorrow, and I am to put the message on the board.

He stayed another ten minutes, just chatting about this and that. And I can't help it, it seemed so very good to see and talk with him again — so very right, somehow.

I'm not at all surprised that I am no longer in the mood to say yes to Sammy. I had nearly persuaded myself that the only thing not pointing in Sammy's favor was my feelings, and you aren't supposed to be able to go by feelings anyhow. I had also persuaded myself that Mark hardly even knew my name anymore, and that he was very likely interested in Helen.

Tonight I'm not so easily persuaded. Suppose Mark is actually interested in me?

The biggest question is, would it be fair to accept Sammy's offer when I feel the way I do about Mark? If I were a boy, I don't think I would care to go with a girl who loved somebody else. Suppose Sammy and I started going with each other, and time went on, and I still couldn't find the right feeling for him? Wouldn't that result in multiplied indecision and pain?

October 17,

Well, my family's visit is past. I feel quite desolate again after living in such luxury the last several days.

On Friday I dismissed school early, as planned, and went to meet them at the bus station. My stomach was tied up in knots by two worries. The first and foremost — could I bear the disappointment if they didn't show up? And second — how would I react if and when I did spot their familiar faces among the other faces at the bus depot? Would my emotions give way to a crying fit or something? The last thing I wanted to do was to make a show like that. I wanted to welcome them with shining eyes and a beaming face and perfect composure.

Well, the closer we got, the more jittery I became. I knew we were a little late, and sure enough, just as we drove in, I caught a glimpse of Dad's spectacles, Mom's small, round figure, and Ervin and Joanne standing beside the bus. And sure enough, just like that, I could feel the flood gates wavering and threatening to break loose.

They saw us at once and came hurrying over. I blinked as hard as I could, and tried to smile a bright welcome. Just as I was ready to give up trying not to break down, I spotted a little pixie face peeping from behind Dad, and then a little streak came running for my arms. Elizabeth! Anyhow, she shocked me out of my tears and saved my day.

If I would write from now to the end of this school term, I don't believe I could get down in words how great it felt to be among my own again, to hold Elizabeth in my lap and be nearly smothered by her hugs and kisses, to laugh and talk all the way back to Grandpas.

One of their first questions was, "How's school going?" I told them I wanted to forget about school and just enjoy them for awhile.

Of course, Grandpas and Crists all crowded around when we got back — I resented it because I wanted them to myself. Friday evening Crists were here for supper, and after dishes Joanne and I were naughty and sneaked up to my room for a while to do some talking. I told her about Sammy's letter, and without really meaning to, also spilled a little about Mark. After awhile Ervin came up and Joanne told him all about it, which made me feel awfully silly. As I had predicted, they didn't have a whole lot of advice to give me. Ervin did say that he thinks he is going to give Mark a hint. I told him if he does, I'm going to disown him for a brother-in-law. I trust he took the threat to heart.

Saturday evening, Dad, Mom, Ervin, Joanne and I had another good talk, a little about Sammy's letter, but mostly about school. I finally broke down and told them the whole story. I had the crying spell then that I had escaped on Friday.

I felt like I used to years ago when I was hurt or unhappy and Dad and Mom took me on their laps and comforted me. I was reminded again that no matter what, my family would stand behind me, comforting and sympathizing.

I hate to have them worry about me, though. Mom will probably be thinking about me day and night and fearing that this will all be too hard on me. The fuss those people had about my weight loss! It was sort of fun to watch them stare at me and shake their heads. I am very much disappointed though, because they all agreed that because of my big frame, I look much better a little on the plump side. Dad even had the nerve to tell me I look like a sick horse with my bones sticking out all over! What a let-down to learn that I will never be small and slender — only either big and plump, or big and skinny.

Helen, Joanne and I had a nice time at church yesterday afternoon.

And this morning they did come to visit school for a few minutes before leaving for home. Benny pulled a few fantastic faces, Arthur looked like a stone wall and Loretta Sue like a sour pickle, but otherwise things didn't go too badly.

October 20,

I just got done sealing and addressing the envelope that contains my answer to Sammy.

I wrote him how undecided I've been, and that for the time being, my answer is no. I tried to make it as nice a letter as one can be with such a message. Even so, he will never know how hard it was for me to write it, and how much I really do care for him, as a very good friend and neighbor. He will probably think, like Joe, that I am a heartless girl who enjoys turning down boys. Will he react like Joe did? I don't think I could take it if he did.

Did I do the right thing, or didn't I?

October 22,

Back to school troubles —

I have been suspicious for awhile that some mocking has been going on behind my back, with Becky and Sarah Helmuth as targets. I shrank from investigating for fear that some serious problem would come to light, and we have enough of those to keep me busy.

Today at recess, I discovered most of the upper grade boys (except Arthur who was at home helping his dad husk corn) had formed a half-circle around little Sarah, all chanting, "Hollow head, hollow head." Just like that, Benny reached out and gave her a push that sent her flying into the mud. When Sarah began sobbing heartbrokenly, the chant changed to "Crybaby, crybaby."

I am by nature a fairly level-headed person, but the sight of those great, strong boys making fun of a helpless little girl, made my blood pressure shoot up dangerously high. I was trembling with righteous indignation as I marched up to the unsuspecting Benny and shook him hard. I comforted Sarah a little, and then glared at the circle of boys.

"Boys," I said, and my voice dripped with quiet anger and contempt. "Boys, isn't there a man among you? How low-down, how small can you be? I want you all to come inside and sit down in your places."

I turned my back and marched into the schoolhouse, walked up through the empty classroom, my shoes clomping decisively against the wooden planks. I sat down in my chair, and suddenly my anger and bravado were gone. I was left with a feeling of weakness and despair.

I waited, sending a desperate, wordless prayer heavenward. The door banged open and I could hear the shuffling of feet coming up the aisles, and then all was quiet. I don't know how long we sat in that breathless stillness. I didn't dare look up. I was afraid of what I might read in the eyes of the boys in front of me. Finally, their very silence encouraged me. I looked up — looked at each boy in turn and was surprised to see the sheepishness in the eyes watching me. I felt a rare wave of love and pity for them all. Weren't they just boys after all? Surely, somewhere in their hearts was a soft spot that could be touched.

"Boys," I said in a low voice. "I'm sorry I lost my temper. Please forgive me. I'm sure you all have the makings of men in you."

I reminded them of the warnings in the Bible against mocking, of the prophet Elisha, the forty-two children, and the two she-bears. Then I asked them to write a note of apology to Sarah and to stay in the rest of the noon hour. They seemed willing to take their punishment, and it's hard to believe, but I'm pretty sure I saw Benny wipe a few tears. All the love I've been longing to feel for my pupils these long weeks of school came pouring into my heart. I longed to give them all a few comforting pats on the head.

I rang the bell then, and for a few glorious hours I realized once more the joy of cooperation from my pupils. Those boys were jewels all afternoon, and Loretta Sue and company seemed also strangely subdued. For a few hours, my dying teaching ambition received new life. For a few hours, I was once more the teacher at Sunnyside, cheerful, loving, giving each pupil special attention and special smiles, exerting myself to make the lessons exciting and interesting. And the pupils responded.

But it was for a few hours only. Nearing time for

dismissal, Arthur came with the buggy to take home his brothers and sisters. He tied his horse to the hitching post and came into the entrance. I was helping Ephraim look for his coat at the back of the room when I heard Arthur ask, "What did you play at noon?"

Someone answered, "Nothing." They moved on outside, and then came the sound I dreaded, the sound of a group of boys laughing derisively. Sick at heart, I edged closer in time to hear Arthur's voice, "You wouldn't have caught me writing an apology to that little sissy."

I should have gone out then and there, and made him come in and write one. If it had been one of the other boys, I probably would have, but since it was Arthur, I pretended I hadn't heard it.

What is there about Arthur that commands such awe from his classmates, and causes even his teacher to be afraid of him? If it weren't for Arthur's influence I think I could do something with this school. There is such a complete change of atmosphere when he is absent.

The ironic thing is that Arthur hardly ever makes a mismove himself, or if he does, he is sly enough to do it behind my back. He only encourages the other boys with that silent smirk of his, an occasional few words, or a wink, and lets them be the ones to get into trouble and bear the consequences.

Oh, Arthur, Arthur, if you could only realize what you are doing.

October 28,

What a gorgeous autumn day. Blue, blue skies with a few white clouds. Steve would call them blobs of mashed potatoes, or whipped cream, or ice-cream. (Umm, I'm hungry.)

Today we went to church. Melvin Glick preached the main part. He is not exactly a talented or fluent speaker, but what he says means something, and you can see it comes from the heart. But as he preached, I could not help noticing Benny seated on the bench a few feet away, busily engaged in wiggling, whispering and showing off his latest face-making feats. And Arthur, chewing gum a few benches away.

After church Polly cornered me and asked the dreaded question, "How are you getting along with our children in school?"

How was I to tell this gentle-faced, bowed-down woman that their children were causing me sleepless nights and worries without end. "I-I-I-" I began and looked up helplessly at Polly. She was watching me intently, and took away from me the words I couldn't find.

"I know, Lois," she said brokenly. "I can see it in your face. Our children are causing you trouble. Is that right?"

I had to nod my head.

"I should have asked you before, but I kept hoping — hoping that things were going better this year. I thought perhaps you would win them over with your tact and friendly ways. Oh, Lois, what are we doing wrong? We've tried and tried to train our children the right way, but —"

I can't put in words how it made me feel, seeing that little woman crying out her heartache for her children. My trials seemed suddenly so trifling in comparison. My stay at Shady Rill is temporary, but these children are hers forever, her own flesh and blood, and she must love and long over them with all of a mother's love.

But why — Why this contrast between parents and children? It is a mystery to me. What causes their children to be so defiant of authority? Is there some way to get it out of their systems? I can say that I no longer feel toward my pupils as I did at the beginning of the term. I am beginning to care for them deeply. They are no longer just a bunch of disgusting children. They are <u>my</u> children, children with precious souls who have many good points that need to be encouraged and developed.

I read somewhere that there are no good children, and there are no bad children — only happy children and unhappy children. And my heart cries out in pity for the unhappy children in my school.

I haven't mentioned that I'm planning a trip home over next weekend. They are planning to have communion services then.

I wanted to get Helen to substitute for me on the days I won't be here, but now she has a job as a hired girl.

It's not right to sit inside on a day like this, when it seems as though nature is giving us a few last chances to soak in the sun and to revel outdoors before the days of ice and snow and storm. I'm going to take out my writing pad, and sit in a nest of leaves in the woods, and perhaps write a bit, and think and dream.

With the evening sun just shining,
In my dreamy, upturned face,
And the lumps of fleecy whiteness
Sailing on in endless space,

While the leaves are gliding downward,
Hues of golden, green, and red;
Softly, softly, without rustle,
Settling in their winter bed.

With the charms of autumn's splendor
Sweeping o'er me like a breeze,
Here I sit in blessed quiet
Underneath the maple trees.

And the presence of my Maker
Fills my soul with soothing song,
Whispering of peace and beauty,
In a world of hurt and wrong.

And the worries that harrassed me,
And the burden of the day,
Softly, gently, like the eagle
Take on wings and fly away.

November 2,

Give me, oh give me, the old white house,
On the sloping side of a hill,
With its battered sides and -- ------- and?

How sad indeed! My poetic streak has died before I've finished the first verse. Just as well, since I see that I've used the word 'sides' twice already, and it sounds as though it's the hill that's battered instead of the house.

For the first time in my life, I'm doing my diary writing aboard a Greyhound bus. I'm amazed at how readable my handwriting is in spite of it all.

By the way, journal, I hope you won't think I'm so emotionally attached to you that I could not bear to leave you a couple of days. You just managed to come along by mistake, because your absentminded owner got you mixed in with a 'going home' pile of items, and then later stuck the whole pile in her suitcase. I don't dare think of what would happen if Aunt Katie or someone got hold of it. (Uncle Crists are traveling with me, by the way.)

Ach, why do I pretend to be in a journal-writing mood, when I can think of only one thing. I'm going home! Chug on, you Greyhound. Every mile is bringing me closer home. Closer, closer.

I wonder how I will feel in a few days from now when every mile will be taking me further away from home?

Congratulations—to myself. I've come up with a poem after all, short and simple though it be. Here it is:

Home, home, home,
Home, home, home.
All that's good,
And all that's fine,
Is repeated in this line,
Home, home, home!

November 5,

I've been home, and now I'm going back. I have been home, and for a while have been with my own—

"Every mile is bringing me closer home."

my own family, friends, pupils, church. I have talked with them, laughed and smiled about joyful things, wept with them in their sorrow for a few days again. Together we listened to the word of God preached in the familiar voices of the home ministers; together we partook of the bread and wine, and washed each other's feet as a symbol of brotherly love.

I've had a wonderful visit. Nearly everybody I met treated me like a long-awaited queen of some kind. Steve was sure it would all go to my head but I told him that a few days at Shady Rill would take care of that.

There was not enough time. I just barely squeezed in my special visits with Dad and Mom, Joanne, Steve, Annie, Ruth, and Mary.

I can't say that I wanted a personal talk with Annie. Something made me want to shy away from her as far as possible, and I could see that she was avoiding me, too. We were friendly to each other, sure, but it was the strained, formal friendliness of strangers, not of 'almost' sisters. I could hardly force myself to look her in the eyes. (Traitors usually have a hard time doing that.)

It was the same way with her mother, and of course, with Sammy, too. When I did happen to encounter Sammy's eyes, against my will, they looked even more hurt and lost than I had imagined they would. He talked with his eyes in those few seconds. I have discovered that Joe Miller's kind of reaction wasn't nearly as hard to take as Sammy's is. Have I made a mistake? Have I? Is there no one who can answer that question for me?

Rather strange to think that had I answered Sammy's letter with a yes, we would probably have had a date yesterday evening.

I got to visit Sunnyside this morning for a few short minutes before it was time to leave. Needless to say, I felt very much at home. What quiet orderliness.

Ruth is as charming as ever and makes a very efficient teacher. I still think she and Steve would make a good match.

Carolyn climbed up on the seat beside me just now and is trying to get me interested in her chatter. I might as well lay aside my pen and give her some attention.

Later— she's gone back to Papa and Mama to eat a cookie and an apple so here we go again.

I didn't know Aunt Katie could be such a friendly, smiling genial person. This trip must be doing her good. It would be very easy to like her if she would always be this way.

Have we ever got an assortment of people in this bus. I've been trying to spot a happy, peaceful-looking face among them— in vain. There's a woman in the seat ahead of me who makes the shivers go up and down my back. Her hair looks as though it has been dyed several times, with streaks of black and yellow and red. Red paint on wrinkled cheeks, hawk nose, and painted eyelids. But her eyes are what is haunting—so wild and hopeless.

A few seats back is a couple having a quarrel— a real nasty one. Their language makes me cringe.

I'm too lazy to describe any more of the weirdos in here, but there are quite a few. I wonder what the life story is behind them, and what circumstances brought them to where they are now. How can we be thankful enough for our Christian heritage?

Going traveling like this and getting glimpses of the world in its misery and wickedness, is sobering. One must wonder— how long? How long until an end will be spoken to it all? And what all must happen before that end shall come?

My thoughts are traveling full speed, churning and jumping from one thing to the other. Right now I am thinking of the boys who didn't take part in Communion yesterday. Joe Miller was one of them. Somehow, it was discovered they were involved in drinking and smoking. The community was shocked. I thought I could just feel the touch of sadness in the air. What a let-down, what a shame, what a tragedy when we who are to be a chosen people, a light to this dark world, instead choose to be a part of the world. God be merciful to us.

To get back to schools. It was very good to see my former pupils at Sunnyside, but right now my thoughts go forward— to my pupils at Shady Rill. God has answered my prayers in at least one way. He has put love in my heart for these pupils who need it so much.

This little vacation has given me a chance to breathe and think things over, and I feel refreshed and renewed. Yesterday in his sermon, Ivan Eash told the story of the Israelites and how they faced the walls of Jericho. I thought at once of the rebellion and disobedience at Shady Rill that looms ever before me like the great and mighty walls of Jericho. And a new hope was born within me—of someday seeing the Jericho walls at Shady Rill crumbling and breaking down at last.

November 10,

Dear God, you have given us a small victory. Thank you, oh thank you, for your help in spite of our weakness. And grant that each victory will help us win the next one.

It's a long story, journal, and the thought of writing it all makes me weary, but my habit of recording everything of importance is strong, so I'll begin.

We arrived back here at Grandpas Monday evening around five o'clock. First thing I glanced over to the schoolhouse and saw that substitute Norma Troyer's buggy was still parked in the school yard. After chatting a bit with Grandpa's I decided to run over and enquire how things had gone in my absence. I didn't relish the job, because my sixth sense informed me things had hardly gone too well.

Norma was sweeping the classroom. I thought her eyes looked a little swollen, but I pretended I didn't notice and asked her how she had managed. The tears started rolling down her cheeks.

"I- I didn't manage," she sobbed. "How can you take it? They're simply awful!"

It took awhile to get her started, but when she did start, she could hardly stop. The pupils were brats, all nineteen of them. They had talked out loud in school, they hadn't stayed in their seats, they had thrown paper wads. The boys had put a live mouse in her desk, they had thrown a part of her lunch down the privy hole, they had climbed the trees and stayed there all recess in spite of her pleading and threats, they had talked back and laughed her in the face, and called her an old grouch.

I listened in horror. Surely, not even Shady Rill

pupils would be outlaws like this. Surely, surely, they hadn't been as bad as Norma thought.

I walked about as in a dream all evening. With each passing minute, the Jericho walls seemed to grow bigger and blacker and uglier before me, mocking and taunting me, blocking out all sunshine, all hope of ever seeing them crumble at my feet.

Only a small comfort remained. Evidently the pupils liked and respected me more than they did Norma. They had never acted like that for me, at least. And yet, suppose this was a turning point for the worse. Suppose they _would_ act that way from now on.

At any rate, I knew that the climax had arrived. Something would have to be done—something different, something drastic—something that would shake up these pupils, make them stop and think. But what? What could _I_ do?

I paced the room. I put my head into my hands and cried until my eyes felt nearly swollen shut. I stared out the window into the darkness, and tried to think. I knelt beside the bed and tried to pray, but nothing seemed to bring even one feeble ray of light or hope. There was only the blackness of the wall.

Then I picked up one of Grandma's old poem books lying on the bureau, opened it and mechanically read the poem at the top of the page. I was closing it again, when the words began to soak through.

JESUS AND I

I can not do it alone-
The waves run fast and high,
The fogs close chill around
And the light goes out in the sky.
But — I know we two shall win in the end-
Jesus and I.

I cannot row it myself—
My boat on the raging sea,
But beside me sits another
Who pulls or steers with me;
And I know that we two,
Shall come into port—
Jesus and I.

Coward and wayward and weak—
I change with the changing sky,
Today so eager and brave,
Tomorrow not caring to try.
But He never gives in, so we two shall win—
Jesus and I.

(Dan Crawford)

As never before, I was ready to turn the handling of our sinking boat over to Jesus. But still, I couldn't expect Jesus to do it all. I would have to do my part.

Finally, I got out my pen and scribbling paper and started writing to my pupils. Not that I thought a letter to them would be so effective, or make them stop and think. But it was my natural impulse. When I am as pent up with emotions as I was then, I must write. Writing is my release, my safety valve.

Besides I can't talk. I knew that I could never say the things I wanted to say in front of the classroom with all the children seated before me. For one thing, I would probably break down and cry before I got through the first sentence.

This morning I got up early and reread what I had written. In the morning light, it sounded overly emotional. I crossed out about half of it, and recopied the rest, and took it along to school.

The pupils arrived in their usual fashion, though perhaps a little more boisterous and noisy. I could see that the spirit of the mob was still in some of them.

I rang the bell at the appointed time and the pupils came to their desks. My knees started wobbling. It would have been so easy to shove the whole thing aside and pretend I didn't know about their misdemeanors. How would I begin? Would the children laugh at me as they had laughed at Norma?

I struggled to compose myself, forced myself to look my pupils in the eyes, and to remember that they were only young children who desperately needed help.

Finally my voice box let out a squeak and I got started. I told them that instead of having our usual morning devotions we would talk for awhile instead. Then I got out the letter and read it aloud.

I think I'll copy it here, just for the record in later years.

Dear Pupils,

It is nearly midnight. Perhaps I am doing a strange thing, writing to my pupils at midnight, but let me explain.

Tonight when I got back from my trip, I went over to the schoolhouse to talk with your substitute and asked her how she had enjoyed her two days of teaching. What she told me, hurt me very much.

Tonight I have been thinking about you all a lot, and about our school year so far. A school should be a happy place of working together—of helping each other, and learning how to grow up to be strong men and women. Our school has not been such a place.

On my way home on the bus, I watched a little boy and his mother and father. His parents looked angry and they were fighting and quarreling, saying all kinds of mean things to each other. The little boy started crying, and his mother pushed him away. His father slapped him on the mouth.

I had to pity that little boy. He will probably grow up to be unhappy like his parents, fighting, hating, and living in sin.

We have a better chance than that little boy. We can hear about God every day, we can go to chuch, we can go to a Christian school if we choose. The path to faith and love and peace is open before us.

Do we then want to throw away these blessings God has given us, and live the wretched way of the world? Do we want to grow up too weak and cowardly to stand up for the right? Too full of pride to be able to give up our self will to each other, our parents, teachers, and God?

I think we all want to grow up to be among the few brave, God-fearing men and women in the world. And to grow up to be that, we must start now.

You know, back home at church on Sunday, one of the ministers told us the story of the Israelites and how they conquered the mighty walls of Jericho. I'm sure you all know the story.

Let's imagine we are the Israelites and that the rebellion and disobedience in this school are the great and mighty walls of Jericho. God wants us to get those walls out of the way, because as long as they are standing He can not bless us. We will not have a happy school and we will not be happy ourselves.

But Joshua couldn't move the walls of Jericho alone and God didn't do it alone. All the Israelites had to help. That was the only way they could budge those stubborn walls. And that is the only way God can help us budge the walls here at Shady Rill— if we all pitch in and help.

We might as well admit it, we could all have done better. I can see many places where I failed to be the teacher I should have been, and I hope you can forgive me.

It is our choice— we can begin knocking down these walls by admitting that we were wrong, by being cheerful, respectful, and loving from now on, or we can help Satan build these big, ugly walls bigger and uglier by doing just the opposite.

I would like to ask you two questions. I will give you a piece of paper and then I want you to answer them as honestly as you can.

1. Are you willing to do all you can to help us make our school a better, happier one?

2. Do you have any suggestions how we can do so? If you do, please write them down.

When I finished reading, I looked up, meaning to add a few more words, but as I looked over the classroom full of serious faces, it was too much. All my love for them, all that I longed to say and have them understand, came into my voice and choked me. I couldn't say more, so I passed out the papers and prayed that God would soften their hearts.

I think He did. I was amazed at the response of some of my supposed-to-be rebels. Several of them added an apology, including my proud princess, Loretta Sue. To be sure, Arthur wrote only, "I might try," but that was a small damper indeed in the middle of so much encouragement.

Some of the answers were even sort of humorous. Benny wrote, "Norma proply told you we threw her lunch down the tolet hole. We dident even. We just said it to teese her and she beleved it. I'm sorry I climed the trees. I'm glad you came back."

Of course, I'm not so naive as to believe that my problems are over, or that the Jericho walls lie flat on the ground. There is a lot of hard work ahead of us, and perhaps we will lose what we gained. But still— it has been a good day, and I think I can see a crack in the wall.

I will soon be a heap on the floor if I don't get to bed. It isn't that late- we were extra early tonight, but I missed out on most of last night's sleep, and oh, the strain of a day like today.

November 13,

I just got done taking another skim through Grandma's book of poetry. There is something so refreshing about poems; especially old-fashioned ones like the ones in this book, I think. It is fascinating to find one's own thoughts mirrored in the penned words of poets of long ago.

Some of the most stirring poetry, I think, is in the Bible. What words are more sublime than those in the love chapter in 1 Corinthians 13, or in the faith chapter, or in some of David's psalms. And to think that those words written thousands of years ago are still being read by people all over the world.

November 15,

Today was Saturday. The young folks got together at neighbor David Millers to husk corn this afternoon. Most of the young folks stayed for supper and games and you name it, but since I didn't particularly care to take all that in, I came home early. I have a feeling it'll probably turn out to be a real party.

I didn't even enjoy the afternoon very much. Most of the time I spent husking in the company of two very silly young girls and a tight-lipped boy whose

". . .I think I can see a crack in the wall."

names I barely know.

I got two glimpses of Mark, one when he came, and one when he left. I don't think he ever looked in my direction. And— he left early too, and Helen went with him. Of course, it only makes sense since he drove right past her home and she had no other way. I ought to be downright ashamed to let it bother me but I can't seem to stop. The conviction keeps growing that they care for each other, and might in fact, already have something going.

I should quit nursing my little heartache and turn my attention to school. Thank God it is a more cheerful thought than it used to be.

There are still problems though, and so many things that need working on. Arthur is still Arthur, Rob still Rob, Benny still a monkey, and Loretta Sue hasn't entirely laid down her high and mighty air. But there is a different atmosphere, difficult to analyze, unless it is simply that the children are beginning to like me and aren't afraid to show it. To my love-starved heart, that covers a multitude of sins.

Possibly, part of the difference also lies in the fact that I'm beginning to teach with my heart, instead of mechanically going through the motions.

Strange, but I find it harder to be strict enough than ever, when I know that as a whole they are trying so hard. Since the walls of Jericho seemed to make an impression on the pupils, I decided to take it one step further. I got them to help me make a picture of a big wall, and then worked out a point system having to do with either adding to, or tearing down the wall. Quite a sizable piece has been done away with already.

It has made a definite improvement in behavior, but pity me, the judge. It is a strain to try to be fair at all times, and how mean I feel to put back one of those hated black blocks because of a small classroom cut-up, or an angry word. Teaching is hard work, any way you look at it.

One thing bothering me is my lack of communication with the parents. So far I have received no direct opposition, but we ignore each other entirely too much. I haven't exchanged a dozen words with some of them.

Last week I didn't feel right letting the ones involved in all those nasty pranks go scot-free, so I sent home notes to their parents, asking them for their opinions and advice. I got in return two very nice notes from parents offering their full support, and two from parents who evidently would rather not have been bothered.

I might as well quit trying to focus my thoughts on school, lay my diary aside, and brood about Mark and Helen in earnest. This is what I get for looking down on flighty girls who lose their hearts and heads all for the sake of a boy. It appears as though I've gone and done the same thing.

November 18,

I'm lonely tonight. Homesick, I guess.

I'm finding out that it is hard to love, and be perfectly quiet about that love, to force it back into a little corner of the heart, keep it there, perhaps for life, cramped and smothered and choked to death, when it could blossom into a lovely thing were it only allowed to live and grow.

But such is life. How perverse it is. Why can I not feel that love for someone who loves me, instead of reserving it for someone who doesn't need or want it?

I try to persuade myself that I am very happy, both for Mark and for Helen, (if there is something to their friendship) and then just at the point when I've nearly succeeded, there's my ugly Self sticking up its head and whimpering, "But what about me?"

November 29,

Here is a copy of a letter I found in my lunch bucket tonight.

> "Dear teacher Lois,
>
> At last I am writing you. I wanted to for a long time and I couldn't get up enough nerve.
>
> I want to say again that I am very sorry for the mean things I did this year. I did some things behind your back, and once I said something mean about you. I didn't mean it but I was afraid Loretta Sue wouldn't be my friend if I liked you.
>
> Sometimes I whispered and twice we passed notes. I hope you can forgive me, though I am not worthy of being forgiven. I want to except any punishment you give me.
>
> It is bedtime now. I hope I can sleep better now since this is off my mind. It has bothered me very much. If I die before the night is over, I hope I can go to heaven. Last night I dreamed the end of the world

was here, and I saw you go to heaven, but
I had to go to hell.

I am glad you are our teacher.

With love,
Anna Marie Glick

I sat down right after school and wrote her a return note.

My poor dear children. I'm not the only one under pressure. They are too— under peer pressure. How I wish I could take away all the struggles and temptations life still has in store for them. Oh God, take care of my children. My Benny, my little Ephraim, my Robbie, Arthur, Loretta Sue, Anna Marie, and all the others. Why must they have so many deep-seated problems, be so full of unhealthy attitudes in their supposedly carefree, innocent years of childhood? I am so afraid for some of them— so afraid that the deep-seated problems will not leave them as they grow older; so afraid that they will forget to turn to God for the peace and happiness they are looking for.

Oh God, if there is anything, anything, that I can do to influence these tender young souls in the right way, then help me to be willing to do it.

December 7,

Bbbrrrrrrrrrrrrrrrr! Winter has arrived in fullest fury, with its below zero temperatures and blasts of snow. Right now Mr. Wind is having a bad temper tantrum, shrieking around the house corners and banging against the window. I am curled up in bed with one of Grandma's woolen blankets wrapped around me. It is delightful to be so toastily warm in spite of all the icy, threatening things the wind keeps yelling at me.

I have discovered a gold mine. Yesterday evening Grandpa and Grandma got started with one of their laughable, good-natured arguments. Grandpa insisted that a certain record-setting blizzard had occurred in the year so and so, and Grandma said it most certainly was in the year so and so. Finally Grandma hobbled over to the bureau and dug from out of an assortment of old books and papers, a whole stack of journals. (My eyes popped greedily at the sight.) She soon proved Grandpa wrong, and then went on reading and chuckling— and ended up letting me have the journal she wrote when she was about my age.

I read most of it last night, and finished tonight. It was as though someone took my hand and led me backwards— backwards down the years to Grandma's day. I saw Grandma as Miss Martha Miller, living at home with her family, a lively blue-eyed girl who loved to work outside. Then along came David Yoder, the bashful, gangling neighbor boy, and asked for her hand in marriage. Hard-hearted Grandma refused, but Grandpa didn't give up easily, and in the end won his prize. (Oh, oh, does that have a special meaning for me?) Then they were married, and had a little boy named Dad— or I mean Willis, who was very stubborn and needed a lot of spankings. (I'll have to tease Dad about that). After a few more years, Crist was born. That is as far as that diary goes. If I'd dare, I'd ask for and devour all the others. I wonder if the time will come when I'll let one of my granddaughters read this diary.

As I was reading, I started thinking what kind of Grandma I would make, if I ever happen to be one. A few pages later, here was Grandma wondering the same thing. How she would be as a grandma, with wrinkles, and spectacles on her nose.

It's amazing how much her journal sounds like mine- how many of our thoughts and feelings run parallel. Grandma seems suddenly a lot closer to my heart than she ever has before. I have considered her too much as a person living worlds apart from me with her exacting and old-fashioned ideas.

Now at least, perhaps I know where I got hold of this writing streak. I have often wondered why I have this need for writing. When I see or hear something of extra interest or of great beauty or tragedy— something within me cries, "Write it, write it. Get it on paper. Spill it all out." Sometimes I get a burning urge to really write— something more than diary trash that no one will ever read but myself. It makes me restless and dissatisfied with the little good I have done in the world so far.

But why do I feel this way? Other people can go through life happily devoid of the need to write a single line. Am I just full of notions?— sentimental? emotional? I wish I knew.

December 8,

What a dark night. Grandpa and Grandma have retired a long time ago and the house is very still, so eerily still that every noise and rustle I make, makes me jump.

My soul is hungry for the cozy companionship of my family. Just now I am lonely, lonely, lonely. I feel all by myself in this great big world. I know my family and friends don't miss me half as much as I miss them. They still have each other. The little hole I left is hardly noticed anymore. And sometimes I wonder if there is anyone here in __________ who really loves and needs me. I need to be needed. Perhaps my pupils need me, but if I weren't here someone else would probably be there, doing a better job than I can.

My, I'm really in the dumps. I feel like an old granny who has found out that nothing on earth is as wonderful or as hopeful as it seemed to be in youth. Vanity, vanity, all is vanity.

What does the future hold anyhow? Just now it doesn't beckon to me at all. It all seems so hopeless. The world is a seething mass of war and grief, worldliness and unrest, full of sick, sick people. It is frightening to see so-called Christians leaving the faith— it is frightening to see so-called Christian churches indulging in practices and doings that can't be God's will, to see them drifting, seemingly unawares.

How can we be sure that we can be steadfast in these last bewildering times, or that we are on the right track <u>now</u>?

God, you are the only one to turn to. Let us not be blinded to the way things really are. Impart to us of your wisdom. Keep us safe— all my loved ones, so dear to my heart. Enfold us in your care, and keep us safe— and keep us safe.

January 2,

Today was another cold day. My feet felt like two ice chunks by the time we got to church this morning. But I deserve no pity because if I would have put on as many clothes as Grandma wanted me to, I would have been all right.

I don't know if I'll bother going to the singing tonight in this bitter weather. The singings here usually don't make me feel very good anyhow. I haven't gotten used to the giddy rowdiness, and all the other things that go on.

There was a stranger in church today- Lloyd Hanning from Wisconsin, somewhere. He is a young man in his twenties who is interested in joining here. He looks fairly decent, perhaps more so than a lot of the boys here.

I hear Aunt Katie's sharp voice downstairs, and can't help congratulating myself for being up here out of her way. I wish I could learn to accept her the way she is. Part of my resentment against her stems from the fact that I think Crist deserves someone nicer.

I was at Crists for awhile yesterday forenoon helping Aunt Katie get a quilt in frame. I nearly always leave that house, thankful that I do not need to live there. Everything is too clean, too fancy, too unhomelike. The vital spirit of a loving, comfortable family circle is missing. How true that a house does not make a home.

I heard today that Mark will be leaving the community in two more weeks.

January 5,

My Dear Diary!

I don't have time to write much, but I feel that you ought to hear a very special piece of news. It is a piece of news that makes me feel humble and unworthy, grateful and happy, and very much scared.

My dream man has spoken. Mark has asked to take me home next Sunday evening.

He stopped in at the schoolhouse after school, and handed me a letter. Said he'd planned on sending it by mail but then when he found out that he would be coming past here today anyhow, he decided to deliver it personally. Then he was out and gone before I could do more than blink a few times.

Imagine how I felt, opening that letter and reading the contents. I wonder how often I reread it until I actually believed it.

I would rather dream than write.

January 6,

I have been sitting here many minutes, thinking and thinking and thinking some more. I feel like a duck trying to soak up water. It is hard to absorb that Mark actually asked me.

I am happy, but it seems that a person can never be completely happy in life. There is always some sadness in one's heart to mar it. Helen is my good friend. In some ways she seems even closer than Ruth or Annie. Although I try to tell myself that I am very likely mistaken, I'm still pretty well convinced that she does care for Mark. And why shouldn't she deserve him as much as I? Will this come between Helen and me as it seemed to come between Annie and me because I refused Sammy? Will all my beautiful girl friendships be spoiled because of my friendship with Mark?

I shouldn't be writing about Mark as though he were mine before we've even had a date. Mark seems to be the serious type but that doesn't mean that things will work out the way I want them to.

I've written a letter home, telling them about Mark and asked them to write me if they have something against it. I'm not really worried.

I wish Mark hadn't set the date so far ahead. I'm getting to be all nerves, just thinking about it.

January 9,

In a few hours time, Mark and I plan to share our first evening together. Help us, Lord, to spend it in a way that is pleasing to you. Thank you for this gift you have given, and help me to keep in mind that I do not know if this gift is for me to keep, of if it will be taken from me. Help us to know your will. "Oh, Father lead us gently by the hand, Through sun and shadow of the future land. Dim and untraveled, lies the way before; O Father lead us, Lead us, evermore."

P.S. Mark has just left. So far, so good. I was afraid I would be too nerved up to be able to talk. I was too, until I sensed that Mark was just as nervous as I. Then I forgot my state of nerves in sympathy for his, and before we knew it we were thawed out after all.

If nothing happens there is to be a next time. When, I don't know, because he will be leaving for home next Wednesday. But we are planning to write.

January 20,

Tonight I was checking papers after school as usual when Kevin Lee came running over and said I was to be at the phone by four o'clock. Someone from home wanted to talk to me.

Since it was nearly four already, I left right away. Sure enough, I was barely there when the phone began to ring. I picked it up and said "hello" in a small voice I barely heard myself because my heart was pounding so loudly.

Then someone said in a deep, gruff voice, "Hello, is this Miss Lois Yoder?" and I knew it was Steve, trying to pretend he was somebody else.

At first he let on he was calling to tell me they are very decidedly opposed to Mark's friendship. Of course, I didn't believe it, so he finally admitted that the only reason for calling was to let me know that a van load from there was coming through this way, and that I was to let Melvin Glicks know the Ivan Eash family wanted to be there for supper the next evening. Just before he hung up, he added, "Oh yes, there is room in the van for an extra passenger. So I hope to see you tomorrow evening."

So Steve is coming! I've been extra lonesome for him all week.

January 24,

Steve has been here, bringing with him the sunshine of his sunshiny self. It amazes me how he dares to be such a mischief in Grandpa and Grandma's presence. He had them laughing more over his antics than I've ever seen them laugh before.

Both Steve and Ivans visited school on Monday

morning. I was pleased with my pupils for a change. They sang and recited their poem and behaved very well as long as Ivans were there. (Steve stayed all forenoon and their model behavior didn't quite stretch that long.)

Steve made a real hit with the boys. He claimed if Benny weren't quite so wild, he'd be a boy after his own heart.

I asked Steve if there is any special girl in his acquaintance, and he tried to let on there isn't. I don't think he knows his own heart.

I wonder when I may dare look for a letter from Mark.

January 26,

I've finally quit laughing. I asked the pupils to write compositions on the subject of animals— any animals in the world. I encouraged them to look through the encyclopedias and try to find an unusual animal that the rest of us didn't know much about. I also told them, by all means, not to copy word for word from their source of information, but to use their own imagination.

The deadline was tonight. I gathered up all the essays after school, forced myself to do my other work and leave the reading and checking of them as an after-supper treat. I was annoyed when the first one went like this.

THE CAT

The cat is an animal. He is small. He can be yellow or black or white or gray or orange. He likes to eat mice. I don't like cats. (Rob)

...And the next one I picked up started out like this.

KANGAROOS

Kangaroo is a furry animal that hops on its hind legs. Kangaroos are the largest members of a group of animals called marsupials. Among most marsupials, including the kangaroo, the females have a pouch on their stomach. They give birth to tiny offspring, which complete their development in this pouch.

This article deals mainly with the five larger species of kangaroos, which are sometimes called great kangaroos....."

Having learned a little about Katharine's intellectual ability, I must believe she was only half listening when I told the pupils <u>not</u> to copy word for word.

The rest were better. Then I came to Benny Glick's sheet. I <u>stared</u> at the title.

SPINKY SPINKY SPOOKADOT

Our teacher said it would be a good idea to write about an animal that not everybody knows about. Do you know about the spookadot? I will tell you about him.

He lives in the Afrecun jungos. He makes his home in the tall grasses. He eats grass and tree bark and fish and monkee tales when they get to close to him. Some people say he looks like a little puppy, but there are some big defernces. For one thing he has stripes, begining at the tip of his long tale. The first strip is brown, then white, then black, then yellow, ornge, pink, purpel, and red and green. His eyes are brite green to. And there are hufs at the end of his feet insted of paws. And another thing, have you ever seen a puppy smile? Some do almost. But a Spookadot smiles all the way. When he is happy he smiles and when he is mad, he opens his mouth big and screems in a turrble loud voice SPINKY SPINKY SPOOK A DOT! And all the lions and tigers and the other animals in jungo put there hands over there ears and are afraid. But he is never mad at little boys. When he sees them he smiles and crawls into there laps and says very quietly spinky spinky spook a dot. I would like to have a spookadot for a pet, wouldn't you?"

Quite a mind-boggler, I must say. I'll have to send a copy to Steve.

Seriously though, I'm kind of impressed. I've been noticing all year that Benny has writing talent. He needs taming down and some teaching on how to use his talent properly, but at least he has that very rare gift of imagination and originality.

I wish he wouldn't be quite so original when it comes to spelling though!

February 3,

Melvin Glicks and Lloyd Hanning were visitors at school today. Melvin gave the children a real rousing talk about their responsibility to be obedient to their parents and teachers.

I hope his own children's ears and hearts were

wide open. They are doing a lot better though.

Lloyd seemed very much interested in all that went on. I could see that not much escaped his eye and it made me nervous. He came up to my desk at recess and asked a few questions about school. He said he had planned on being a teacher himself, until he began being interested in the Amish and decided to come here instead.

He also told me that Mark is one of his best friends and that he misses him.

So do I. I rarely saw Mark when he was still in the community but at least there was always the chance of his showing up somewhere.

I have received no letter from him yet, and it is worrying me. I wish I knew if I misunderstood him or if he misunderstood me, or if the letter got lost, of if he is just taking his time to it.

It tickles me how Grandpa and Grandma both take such an interest in our romance. Grandma told me this morning that if a letter came from <u>him</u> she would prop it up on the top east windowsill, where I would be sure to see it as soon as I got within sight of the house.

Writing is a drag tonight. Good night.

February 4,

Today was a day nearly perfect, weather-wise. I herded out all the children at noon, and tried to get them organized in a game of deer and hound. Halfway through the game, I suddenly thought of something and glanced quickly in the direction of Grandpa's house, toward the east window. <u>Was</u> there something propped against the sill? I found an excuse to run to the far end of the playground and took another long, hard stare. It looked like a letter, all right.

I tried to hurry up time all afternoon and succeeded in making it drag quite a bit. When 3:30 came at last, I felt duly ashamed for having been so impatient and immature. To discipline myself, I forced myself to get the routine after-school work done before I left the schoolhouse.

Sure enough, it was a letter from Mark. Grandma looked very triumphant and smug, just as though she had had something to do with the arriving of it. I brought it up to my room, stared at every mark on the envelope, and decided that I was as nervous and excited about this letter as I was about the first. I did finally get it read, and just now finished rereading, or rather re-rereading it.

It's silly to feel this way, and sillier to write it down, but I've been looking forward to Mark's letter for so long that now that it has arrived, I feel kind of disappointed and let down. There is nothing wrong with Mark's letter (except a few misspelled words, and those don't bother me too much.) He didn't mention having changed his mind about our friendship, as my imagination had nearly convinced me that he would. But it is a short letter, and rather cool. He never referred to me, or to us at all. He only wrote about the work he's doing, the weather, and the visitors at church. Only that between a very formal greeting and good-bye.

I had my letter to him all planned out in my head and could hardly wait till I got his so I could write it. Now I feel chilled. Is Mark having doubts about the whole deal and just couldn't get up enough nerve to write me about it?

I don't know why it took that letter so long to get here.

February 7,

My worry about Mark's letter has worn off a bit. I was probably expecting too much.

I had a refreshing hour after school tonight. Most of the pupils had left except the Glick children, who were rather poky about getting their horse hitched up. Suddenly the door banged open with a great big 'Benny bang' and Benny and a few clumps of snow came flying into the room. He was rolling his eyes and dancing up and down in excitement. "Oh, teacher, quick! A bag!" he said. "We want to catch the rabbit!"

"The rabbit?"

"Yes, there's one in that big pipe out there. I saw his tail go in. Where's a gunny sack or something?"

A gunny bag? I was sure there was nothing like that around. I peeped into the woodroom. Nope. Nothing there. I was ready to suggest that someone run over to Crists, when I spotted an old painting skirt hanging on a nail. I grabbed it, and got a ball of yarn from my desk. With Benny's help, I tied a very secure knot at the end, grabbed my coat and scarf and followed Benny into the excited atmosphere outside, feeling deliciously like a little schoolgirl instead of a stern old schoolmarm.

Anna Marie was tying the horse and buggy to the hitching post and Arthur was standing guard at one end of the pipe, coatless in the biting wind. (He had stuffed his coat into the opening at the other end.)

He grabbed the makeshift bag from Benny and held it over the opening, while Benny and I lifted the other end of the pipe into the air. Nothing happened.

"Thump on it," ordered Arthur.

We thumped, but nothing happened.

"Thump harder."

We thumped harder, but nothing happened. Arthur began making digging remarks about big imaginations, and Benny began looking woebegone. "He was in there," he kept repeating. "I know he was."

"Okay, Arthur," I said. "Why don't you and Benny change places and we'll try one more time."

Benny took the bag, and Arthur got a stick. Thump, thump! Suddenly, Benny was rolling in the snow, clinging to a bag that had become very much alive.

"I got him! I got him!" Benny shouted. "I told you!" He opened one corner of the skirt and peeped in. For once, I think he was so surprised, he forgot to play-act. He just looked genuinely astonished. Then he let out a whoop and nearly let go of the whole works. "Two! There are two rabbits in the bag!"

What an excited chattering.

I told them about a wild rabbit chase David, Steve, and I had one afternoon years ago, how we had chased out eight rabbits in the oats field, and caught not one. Even Arthur laughed about that. Benny promised he would bring along some rabbit meat for my dinner tomorrow because I had helped catch them.

I wish we could always be on such good terms. I wish I could peep behind that elegant, indifferent mask of Arthur's, and see what lies there. It is not hard for me to understand children like Rob and Loretta Sue and even Benny, but Arthur is too complicated for me.

February 9,

Yesterday morning, Benny didn't come to school with the promised rabbit meat for me, but Anna Marie brought me a note from Polly, asking if I would like to come to their place for supper to help them eat it.

So I drove over last night, all by myself through the almost dark. When I arrived at Glicks there was a light in the barn, so I unhitched and bravely took out my horse. Arthur and Benny were working in a corner, pounding away at some pigeon cages. I asked if I could see the pigeons and they showed me a whole roomful of them of all shapes and sizes. I was flabbergasted when not only Benny, but also Arthur voluntarily offered me enough information concerning pigeons to make my head reel.

We had our bunny supper with all its trimmings—mashed potatoes, pork and beans, gravy, ice cream and pie. After supper Arthur and Benny started playing table tennis. I watched for awhile, and then said I would like to play the winner. I ended up getting very much involved in a hot game with Arthur. He won, but just barely.

It was while we were playing that it came to me that this good-natured young gentleman was not the sullen, frigid Arthur I knew at school. For the first time I was seeing Arthur without his mask— Arthur as he was meant to be.

I let myself hope just a little that from now on the relationship between us would be different, but today at school Arthur wore his mask as usual.

February 11,

Tonight is one of those times when the weight of teaching school seems to be choking me. If only I could be assured that I am handling things as they ought to be handled— that I am doing all that can be done for the benefit of this school.

My boys are such unpredictable creatures and have such contradictory sides to them that I am confused. For instance, Benny wrote an essay the other day of things he plans to do when he grows up. He concluded with these words, "It would be nice to be rich and have a big farm, but that is not what I want the most. What I want the most is to be a good man who obeys God. My dad says that is most important."

The next day I had to punish him for using filthy language on the playground and for sassing back when I rebuked him.

Yesterday, I overheard Arthur rebuking some of the younger boys for cutting wild capers during recess. Next time he'll probably encourage them.

It is when I see the good sides of my pupils that I most long to help them. And I keep wondering, am I using the right approach?

It seems as long as I keep rigidly on guard, things coast along fairly smoothly. But I get tired of being on my toes all the time, of putting my best into every minute of the day. It is so easy to relax a bit, to be a little lazy. And then just so soon, I am dismayed that things are once more getting out of control and it is time to crack down again.

I do try to stick to a well-mixed combination of firmness, tact, and love, but perhaps I am too easy with my pupils— too careful to avoid anything that would cause an issue, too conscious of keeping on the pupils' good sides. I know some people would dive right in there and start hacking away at the bad spots without worrying about tact, or about letting the sparks fly.

I find it so hard to be stern. Am I too soft? I wish someone would tell me.

February 15,

My moods surely change. (No wonder, when my pupils' moods seem to change so fast.) Yesterday morning the pupils had a rare singing spree, and sang as though they really enjoyed it. We sang for quite awhile and when Rob chose and started the song, "Round the Walls of Jericho" with a smile in my direction, I thought I could actually hear a mighty crash of crumbling walls.

Then this afternoon Helen and I went visiting the other two schools in the neighborhood. Aunt Katie offered to substitute while I was gone. I accepted the offer with misgivings, but I figured she should be able to manage for a few hours. Besides, just then I was sure my pupils had been reformed to near angels.

By the time we were done visiting schools, my estimation of our school had climbed a few more steps. I could see that my school was definitely not the only one with problems. Pride perched at my ears and whispered that my way of working with the children was by all appearances, the better way.

With flags sailing, I came home and met Aunt Katie who had my pride torn to shreds in less than five minutes. The pupils had not behaved themselves, and Katie's nerves were worn to frazzles. What really bowed me down was that she had caught the boys in the woodshed, smoking a pack of cigarettes. Impertinent Benny told her that it wasn't the first time they had done it.

And tonight, with my pride out of the way, all the school's imperfections come marching before me—and I know that my problems have not disappeared. They are still lurking in every corner, waiting for a moment when I am not on guard.

I am discouraged. My pupils have not changed. I have not really helped them. I have been able, to a certain extent, to gain their respect. That respect often keeps them from doing things openly that they know I disapprove of. But what real good have I done if that respect is lost as soon as I am out of sight? If I have not been able to teach them to show respect for everyone?

What good have I done as long as my pupils obey only because they have to, and not because they have learned to listen to the voice of their conscience? When I have been unable to rid them of those unhealthy attitudes they so stubbornly cling to? When I have been unable to convey to them the beauty of submissiveness, of unselfishness, of honesty, and clean living, of the beauty of a life lived for God, and the hopelessness of a life lived for self.

Have my efforts been in vain? All year I have been trying to reach my pupils. Is there any use to keep on? Is there any use?

February 16,

I was pretty blue about everything this morning, and was half-heartedly going through the motions of being a teacher, when fourth grader Betty held up her hand. "I can't make this one come out right," she said in a whining voice, pointing to a long division problem. "I've gone over it five times, and I don't think it's ever going to come out right." Then unexpectedly, she looked up at me, smiled through her near tears and said, "But I guess I'll keep on trying."

Today I heard several remarks and saw some frowns that revealed a dislike for Bible stories and German singing. It seems hopeless to think of changing their attitudes. I am afraid my words don't penetrate farther than the first section of their ears, but... I guess we will keep on trying."

February 17,

Poor diary's getting a pretty steady diet of school, but tonight I must write a few pages about the rewards of teaching!

We got wet, wet snow today. It was tracked into the porch (not to mention the schoolhouse) and by tonight, dark puddles of muddy water covered the floor.

I told the sweepers that I would clean the entrance tonight, since it was so messy. I thanked them for sweeping and settled down to work at my desk. I was pretty wrapped up in it, until I suddenly caught the sound of a little splash-gurgle out in the porch. Was someone still out there? I was too lazy to look, but I listened and kept hearing faint noises. Then I heard the door open and close, and my curiosity got the best of my laziness. I tiptoed down the aisle and opened the door. A spotless entrance floor gleamed up at me with a proud sparkle. In the corner stood a pail full of black water, with a wadded up rag nearby.

I tracked across the wet floor to the window, and watched Rob run lickety split down the road. Tears came to my eyes. It was one of those special, special moments.

To think that Rob was man enough to lay down his pride and wash up my dirty entrance floor for me! I have a feeling it was his way of apologizing for the happenings of the other day.

If he were a girl, I would thank him profusely tomorrow and tell him how he made my day. Since he's a boy, I'll hardly dare mention my appreciation, for fear of embarrassing his manly dignity. I wonder if boys really don't like to be praised or if it's all a cover-up.

February 18,

I'm spending the evening up in my blue room for a change. This week I was a guest at four different homes, four evenings in a row. That rabbit supper at Glicks really started something.

They have been four interesting evenings, which have helped me get to know the parents better. They have also been revealing. I was at Bert Troyers the first evening and soon understood why their children are the way they are— noisy, unmannerly and inclined to be a little sloppy. Mr. and Mrs. Troyer are one of the jolliest, friendliest and most easy-going couples I've met. There was an overall comfortable, informal atmosphere, but you could see that their children were used to doing pretty well as they wished. After supper the smaller children played some running games in the house, and what an uproar!

The second evening found me at David Millers (Loretta Sue's parents). The atmosphere there was as formal as Troyers was informal. Everything was precise, from Loretta Sue's family themselves, to their knick-knack covered house, to the elaborate dishes of food on the table and to all else within sight or sound. And I, the petrified country mouse, crept away from that citified place as soon as I dared.

The next evening I went home with Sarah and Emma, my two little girls with the look of the hunted rabbit in their eyes. We were met at the door by their mother, and before she even welcomed me in, she was apologizing for the messy house, about the dirty apron she was wearing, the poor supper she was planning, and so on and so on. Thus, she lamented the whole evening, until I no longer wondered why her girls seemed tied down with such inferiority complexes.

One thing I found out though, is that in spite of faults, and my first judgements concerning their indifference, these families do care what happens to their children. All three of the women found a quiet corner to ask me how their children were behaving in school.

It is easy for me to see why the children of the above-mentioned parents have the problems they have. But what about a family like Melvin Glicks? What is wrong there?

I disagree with Aunt Katie. I'm not saying that they're the perfect parents, and I don't know all the circumstances, but I do know that they are trying so hard— and they are hurting because of the way their children act.

I think I have learned a few things in the past few months. One is to follow the age old maxim, "Never judge a person until you have worn his shoes." A year ago I would have been disdainful of a teacher who couldn't handle her pupils. Now that I have worn those shoes and discovered how painful they are, I have revised my thinking. And I choose not to look down on Melvin Glicks because of the struggles they are having with their children.

March 20,

One, two, three and a half weeks since I've dug you out, journal. Time, time where have you flown?

A person looking over the last few pages might get the idea that Mark must not have created a very big splash in my life, as rarely as I mention his name, but I would have you know that that is not the case at all.

The fact is, I'm ready for a good, old-time spill on that very subject, but I don't know where to start. The reason I don't is because there is no explaining the way I feel. Right now I am in half a dozen different moods at once. Try getting that down in explanatory terms.

Sometimes I wonder if I am the same person anymore. If I am the same girl who used to live such a sheltered life with her family in that little white house. So much has changed. So much is still changing, especially since I started going with Mark. I find myself resenting it all. Our friendship is changing even me, and I don't like to be changed.

I don't like the idea of all my old interests growing faint— my interest in school, in writing, and in my friends. I don't like living in a kind of dream world and arousing only at the sight of _him_. I don't like the idea of growing so dependent on a person that I mope when there is no letter from him, and then also mope when there is one in which he has not reassured me in so many words that he still cares for me.

The next thing that is bothering me is Sammy and Helen. I must have a very morbid conscience because I am still worrying about them and imagining that Helen is growing thin and pale.

I also feel a bit guilty because I'm going against the dreams I have half-harbored for so long— of putting in long old-maidenish years of unselfish labor— in teaching, working as a hired girl, and perhaps doing some writing. Since courtship usually brings marriage, those dreams are fast going to smithereens.

And I feel guilty because I got my own way— because things fell into place the way I wanted them to. In most _Young Companion_ stories (and I thought, in real life,) the girl is hardly ever able to get the boy she wants. To run parallel to those stories, Mark ought to have asked someone else. My heart ought to have been broken and bettered by the experience, and in due time, been prepared to accept Sammy and make him a dutiful wife.

All those worries sound fairly self-sacrificing and unselfish. I must confess that there is another worry that is less noble.

I have been to a number of weddings in my life. The brides are always bright-eyed and blooming, radiant with joy. Yet as time goes on, those blossoms in their cheeks fade, and they begin to look tired and a little sick. In a matter of a few years, the brides have a houseful of little children and their time is devoted to changing diapers, cleaning house, washing dishes and making meals. The substance of their conversations is reduced to baby's first teeth, potty training, and the like.

And though I'm not sure I wouldn't like to be Mark's wife someday, the fate of those stout, matronly wives doesn't appeal to me. Their lives seem humdrum and boring.

But those worries are silly little worries. What is really bothering me is something that goes deeper. The seriousness and responsibility of this whole thing is only now beginning to sink in. Am I mature enough and ready for such a step? Are God's blessings on our friendship, or was it only my self-will that made me grab up Mark's offer so soon? How could I have been so sure that Mark is the one for me?

I still don't think Mark's letters sound very enthused, and sometimes I'm not sure about my own feelings either. I'm pining away for him one moment, and the next, I'm doubting my love for him and suspecting that what I have been building on all this time, has only been a fancy-filled infatuation. What if the glamor keeps wearing off the longer we know each other?

What a queer one I am. But I'm feeling better already, even though the pen marks I left behind don't make sense. I've been bottling up for a long time, but something kept me from spilling. I think it was the realization that perhaps someday I would be duty-bound to share my journal with my husband, and I don't want anyone, not even a hubby, to know of my weird notions. But maybe he'll be able to do something I can't— understand me.

March 24,

Oh diary, diary, what strange things was I writing into your pages a few days ago. I daresay it was all some passing nunnish notions.

For Mark has been here and I am still dreaming about brown eyes.

He caught me by surprise for the third time. Saturday forenoon I was washing up the kitchen floor when a knock sounded on the door. Supposing it was someone from Uncle Crists, I didn't bother getting up from my knees, but called out heartily, "Come right on in!" The door opened and when I looked up, I was staring into the slightly red, but smiling face of that— Mark Kauffman!

The shock was nearly too much for me. I scrambled from off my knees, and nearly tripped over my dress. I blushed as usual, and stammered around about my surprise at seeing him, until I had Mark flustered too. He explained that he had written me a letter telling me about his coming, but evidently it had been another slow one.

By this time Grandma came hobbling out, beaming smiles at the two of us, and offered Mark a chair (Something I would have forgotten). She also insisted that he stay for dinner, so I tried hard to get a meal together that would properly impress Mark while he and Grandpa visited in the living room.

Our time together was short, but it was long

enough to set my world Mark-side-up again. I decided that anyone who could spark such a lifting of spirits in me had a rightful place in my life.

April 4,

It is really and truly April. The long, long winter is nearly over. That fact and the touch of spring in the air makes me want to kick up my heels for joy.

I just got done counting the school days left in this term. I got only twenty-one, fewer than I dared hope for. I didn't get out the calendar before, because I knew from past experience that counting days is the surest way to make them pass slowly.

Poor journal gets a back seat in my interests nowadays. By the time I get my weekly epistle off to Mark, my writing well is dry.

I was at home again this past weekend to take in Communion services there. It wasn't so bad coming back this time, when I knew that in a matter of weeks I would be going home for good.

The school board paid me a little visit the other week, armed with loads of praise and flattery. I came closer to considering teaching again here than I ever thought possible. These children have done something to my heart, and the thought of having them go out of my life completely is already beginning to hurt. But in the end I gave a firm no. I'm sorry— I'm ready to admit that this year was good for me, that I learned a lot, and hopefully matured a little, but I would hate to submit myself to another one like it.

And there is a chance after all, that my days of singlehood are not so many anymore. If such _is_ the case (I really don't know), then I would like to spend the remaining ones at home with my family and friends.

April 7,

Ah! The great news at last! I got word today that a little Samuel was born to Ervin and Joanne. If only I could run home and take a look at him. He'll be half grown up by the time I get to see him.

Welcome to the clan, little nephew. May life be kind to you.

April 8,

Another springlike day. I'd like to give the pupils a surprise and take them on a hike as soon as more of the violets and trilliums begin peeping.

School is still a see-saw, giving me rides in rapid succession from cloud number nine to the dust, and from the dust to cloud number nine again. As a whole, things are going well and I am trying to make each day an enjoyable one.

April 10,

Today at last recess the second grade girls wanted me to come out and see a bunch of violets they had found along side the fence. On my way back in, I heard muffled bursts of laughter coming from the horse shed, and after a pause, a chanting, sing-song voice. For a moment I stood in bewilderment. Why, it sounded exactly like— In a flash, I knew what was going on. The boys were getting Benny to imitate Bishop Eli Graber in the middle of one of his sermons.

I moved closer and smiled in spite of myself. It sounded so strikingly like Eli that it was uncanny. Then my smile faded. Benny's voice rose- "Quit your smokin', quit your jokin'. Quit your evil livin'. Repent of all your sinful ways or you will never get to heaven." There were roars of laughter.

I listened, aghast. Didn't these boys realize what a serious thing they were making fun of?

Then came Rob's voice. "I don't care what you say, old preacher. I'm going to get myself a car as soon as I find the money."

"Hush." (Arthur's voice.) "Bout time you make sure teacher's not coming."

Before the footsteps reached the door, I swung it open and nearly collided with Rob. He hastily stepped aside, and I faced the five pairs of startled eyes looking at me.

"Oh, boys," was all I could think to say. I felt like grabbing them by the collars and shaking some sense into them, and stamp their distorted sense of humor into the dust, holding their weakmindedness in front of their eyes and making them see what a mixed-up way they were looking at things.

I turned to Benny. "Whose idea was it for you to imitate Eli?"

Benny let his shoulders and head slump down and said in a sorry, yet defensive little voice, "Arthur's."

I turned to Rob. "Do you really want to buy a car as soon as you have enough money?"

Rob shrugged, squirmed, blinked, and finally blurted, "Arthur said the same thing."

I glanced at Arthur and caught the tail end of a

dirty look traveling in Rob's direction. "When did he say so?" I demanded.

"He often says so. Benny does, too."

I looked at Benny. He shrank against the wall, and then spoke up in self-defense. "I didn't know it was so terrible to say that. A lot of the young folk boys say things like that."

I didn't utter another sound, but turned and rang the bell.

I kept them after school and when I was done talking with them, I asked Arthur to stay a few minutes longer. From the safety of my desk, I studied him hard for a few minutes. What was the expression on his face? Not rebellion or anger as much as an amused indifference. "Knock at me," it seemed to say. "Shout yourself hoarse. You won't get through to me. In fact, I think this is all sort of funny."

I didn't try to knock him down and didn't shout myself hoarse. Instead, I wearily went through the same rigmarole I have gone through before, explaining to him that the boys were doing themselves untold harm by nursing such attitudes and that since he was the leader among them there was a tremendous responsibility on his shoulders. But all the time I was talking, there was a helpless, hopeless feeling in my heart.

This responsibility is getting me down. No— it is not the responsibility. It is the futility of my efforts. I am tired of banging and pushing against this solid Jericho wall. I can't do it alone—not even with the help of the pupils, not even with the help of God. I was wrong. That hateful Jericho wall will never come down—unless the young folks quit influencing their little brothers and sisters the wrong way, unless the parents wake up, and the ministers wake up— unless everybody wakes up and takes action.

Perhaps I shouldn't be writing so forcefully. For who am I ? But when a thing meant to be beautiful is made ugly, when there is a vicious cycle of pure little hearts being warped by their older brothers and sisters' influence and sometimes their own parents, what can a person say?

April 14,

The other day I was over at Uncle Crists and noticed a small bottle standing on the worktable. Absentmindedly, I picked it up, and saw that Aunt Katie's name was on the outside, and that it contained some kind of nerve pills.

Today Grandma and I got to talking about Aunt Katie, and without thinking over my words, I asked about the nerve pills. Grandma admitted that Katie often has bouts of depression, and times when she can't relax enough to sleep.

Having asked one blunt question, and received a satisfactory answer, I decided to keep going. "What do you feel is causing these problems?" I asked next.

Grandma shook her head. "I don't want to judge, but I'm afraid that perhaps Katie has her values a little mixed up sometimes—looking for happiness in the wrong places such as trying to have a beautiful house that is up to date with all the latest fashions, and always spotlessly clean. And then too, Katie had an unhappy childhood, and perhaps the scars still remain. She seems to find it hard to trust people, or to get along with them."

"Has she always been this way?"

"We didn't know her very well until she married Crist. But Lois, you mustn't think your Aunt Katie doesn't have a lot of good points too, because she does. I will have to admit I had a hard time seeing them the first while, and I was often hurt by her sharp words until I learned to follow Grandpa's advice."

"Oh?" I looked at Grandpa, lying on the living room couch, with his eyes half-closed. "Maybe you'll have to pass on that advice to me, Grandpa."

Grandpa sat up slowly and gave me one of his special smiles. "You won't need to ask me, Lois. You can find it again and again in the Bible. Love is always the answer. No one is unworthy of your love. You will meet a lot of people in your life, and everyone of those people will have faults, just as you have—as we all have. Learn to excuse those faults as easily as it is to excuse your own. Look beyond people's dislikable ways, and see the good in them—see them with feelings and needs like your own. Never, never judge a person until you have worn his shoes. God loves all of us, Lois, and he wants all of us to love each other. That is one of the most important lessons in life—to learn to love, and to forgive."

It was one of the longest speeches I've ever heard quiet Grandpa speak. And I know in my heart that the words he spoke are words of deep wisdom. May I never forget them as long as I live.

April 16,

I just got done going through the small pile of letters from Mark. They get to be more interesting and special as time goes on.

I made an interesting acquaintance at church today—Betty Eicher, former teacher of Shady Rill. She taught a total of nine terms here, and quit when she moved out of the community several years ago. I'd guess her to be around thirty-five. She is the spinster of my dreams, jolly, warm and comfortable, and thoroughly wrapped up in her teaching career. The two of us were pulled together like magnets and our conversation of course, centered on the Shady Rillers.

Betty said she had Arthur and his two older brothers, Edwin and James for pupils, and that she remembers Edwin especially well as a lovable little lower grader, mischievous, but sensitive and easily guided.

"I'll never forget the conversation I overheard one day after I punished Edwin for some minor misdeed," she said. "Some of the older boys were gathered in a circle around Edwin, and were taunting him for not being smart enough to do things behind my back. And it still hurts to think of the change that came over Edwin. He ended up being one of my most difficult pupils. And Arthur was a lot the same way."

What a tragedy when such attitudes are passed from friend to friend, from brother to brother, and so on. I am beginning to understand a little of the power of influence.

I need to talk to some cheery, happy-hearted person right now. My thoughts are gloomy and confused.

Today we were asked to remain seated after church services to counsel about several different matters. We girls sat directly behind the menfolk, so I could easily hear them express themselves. They reminded me of a group of quarreling children, each determined not to let anyone else have his own way. How I appreciated the few voices that remained humble and quiet.

Though I have written little about it in here, the conditions in this church have often discouraged me. One hears so much of church splits, bickering and arguing, drift and loose living. Nearly everywhere you go, you can see the tell-tale signs of drift.

I have been reading the old copy of Martyr's Mirror Grandpa has here. It has made me do some deep thinking. Two different pictures keep coming to my mind. One is of those earnest martyrs, giving up all they loved in life to suffer torture and die for Jesus' sake.

The other picture is of us, their descendants. People who don't even have enough nonresistance to get along with their neighbors. People who spend the greater part of their time dolling up themselves and their houses.

When I was younger, I know I had a bit of the conceited notion that we are the only people who are right— God's chosen few. Lately, I believe I am going to the opposite extreme. I keep wondering if God is with us at all, or if we are of the proud, lukewarm Pharisees who deceived themselves. I keep wondering what the apostles or the martyrs would say if they could suddenly rise from the dead, and come to us in this day and age. Would they be willing to accept us as brethren? What would they say about the hate among us, the smoking, drinking, silly jesting and pride? What would Jesus say? What _will_ He say someday?

I keep wondering about myself. Of course, I do try to stay in our church's _ordnung_ and to live a Christian life, but when I compare myself with the martyrs, I feel undone. Why can't I experience more of their zeal and their love to God and fellow men?

I thought I had peace with God, but now I keep questioning God's acceptance of me. What have I been doing for Him? I am making no great sacrifices or suffering for His sake. There is a constant feeling of guilt and unrest in the back of my mind. How can I know for sure? Suppose I am one of those who think they are on the right track, and aren't. The world is full of people who go against the clear teachings of the Bible yet claim to be led by the Holy Spirit, filled with His joy and peace.

And even if I reach my goal, what about all the rest of the people in the world? It seems too sad to think of the millions of souls who will be doomed, perhaps some whom I know and love.

I think of Mark— The Bible says that in the latter times things will wax worse and worse. Suppose we go on to marry, have children, and grandchildren. What will they have to face?

I am too weary to think any longer.

April 23,

I got home from the singing a couple of minutes ago.

Norma Troyer and her special friend were published today to be married. She is one bubbling girl. She must be made out of different stuff than I. Getting married at eighteen and a half, with seemingly no sober thought of the future. I wish her well, but I'm glad it's not me.

The singing tonight was rowdier than usual, I thought. Lloyd Hanning was there, and he didn't look much more at home than I felt.

After we'd quit singing, I was standing in a corner, wishing for a way home when I overheard a group of girls, talking.

"My," says one. "That Lloyd Hanning looks sour tonight."

"Sure does," says another. "He's a little different, isn't he?"

"Yes," says the first condescendingly. "Dad says he wishes such people would just stay away. It seems they can't fit in if they aren't raised Amish. They almost always end up leaving anyhow."

That got me upset.

May 2,

"I'm pressing on the upward way, New heights I'm gaining every day. Still praying as I'm onward bound, Lord, plant my feet on higher ground."

"My heart has no desire to stay, Where doubts arise, and fears dismay——"

I can hear Grandpa singing the above words in his cracked old voice. Right now, I almost envy him.

He must be so much farther ahead on the 'upward way' than I. How would it seem to be so near to the end of life's journey?

I believe I fought one of my hardest spiritual battles these past few weeks. It seemed nearly useless to keep struggling in the Christian life. I was too far from what I should be. It was too hard to keep my relationship with God warm and alive. Too hard to discern right from wrong, too easy to succumb to the world's influences. I was discouraged by the seeming lack of depth in the lives of so many around me.

In my heart I knew these attitudes were wrong. I knew there were many concerned people, still striving to maintain the salt of the earth. And I knew it had to be possible to live for Christ, even in this day and age— even for me. But still I doubted, and the battle continued.

The turning point came last Sunday, when I went home for the weekend. There was a visiting minister there, and both he and Ivan Eash preached powerful sermons, sermons that went straight to my troubled soul. It was mentioned that we live in troubled times, but that God is just as powerful and full of love as He has ever been. The secret is to yield ourselves completely to God's will, trusting him to forgive our sins and lead us ever closer to Him, battle by battle, lesson by lesson. God wants us, as redeemed Christians, to be joyful and full of praise, resting in the confidence that the Shepherd who loved us enough to suffer and die for us, will not abandon the sheep that seek him now. He wants to lead us to green pastures beside the still waters. With His rod and His staff, He will guide us through the valley of the shadow of death. When we stray from Him, He will search the hills and valleys for us, rebuking and chastising if need be. And He longs to someday take us by the hand, talk with us face to face, and show us the glory of His home— and ours.

What a God we serve! Is it not worth all the pain and the struggles to be called the children of such a God? If only I could keep the true vision of my Master in mind. If only I could remember to yield each day of my life in willing service to Him.

But I know how easy it is to forget, to let other things creep in and take first place. Truly the world today is a dangerous place, and we face a great challenge. Just as great, or perhaps greater than the challenge the martyrs have faced down the ages, and are still facing in some lands. There was no compromise for them. Either they had to give up their faith, or their life. And I believe it is just as impossible for us to remain true, without fully yielding our lives to God, as it was for them. Half-heartedness will not stand the test. It is the downfall of our churches. We want to serve God, but we also want to enjoy the pleasures of the world.

May God help us.

May 3,

I got a long letter from Joanne today that contained a diet of mostly Samuel. Sure makes me itchy to see more of the little fellow.

Can I believe it? The school term is nearly ended. A few more days, and I will be closing the doors of Shady Rill behind me, for good.

I can't explain how I feel tonight. So burdened for

my pupils— and already so empty with the realization that my chance to work with them is nearly gone. Where I have failed, I have failed, and there is no changing it.

When I think back to those first days with my pupils, I can hardly believe that they are the same children. Eight months ago, when I looked at them, I saw their outward appearances- eyes of blue and brown, straight hair and curly tops, freckles and pug noses. Mostly I saw their faults and dislikable dispositions.

Today it is different. I hardly notice their outward looks. Instead, I am looking at the inside story of their lives, at their tender children's hearts. I notice with pain that some of them are beginning to harden, some are scarred, bleeding, crying for love and guidance. Today, I find in my heart such a love for each individual that I would like to cry and cry.

What will happen to my little Ephraim, my frustrating heartwarming Benny, and all my others?

It is so unfair. I want those children to grow up to be happy, well-adjusted adults, with healthy attitudes. I want to rest in the hope of meeting them all someday in heaven. But with the influences and peer pressure around them——?

I wonder how many tears I shed this year in behalf of my pupils?

A CHILD'S PLEA

I am a little child...
Small;
Weak and defenseless;
I was born into this world
Not of my own choice.
I could not choose
The kind of parents
Or the type of home
That I'd have liked to have
I am only here—
In a sense, a victim
Of circumstance.

I am a little child——
With a soul
As white as the snow.
With eyes
As clear as the day.
With a mind
Untroubled by cares.
A little child—
The dearest
Sweetest,
Loveliest thing
In all the world.

I am a little child——
More fragile than sheerest glass.
Like a piece of clay
I wait

On the ones who will mold me;
On the ones
Who will be the making,
Or the breaking of me.

I am more precious
Than oceans of gold.
And whether I become
A devil
Or a saint at God's right hand,
Depends
So much on you.
On the things that I see,
The things that I hear—
On the things you imprint
Upon my baby mind.
Beware
A soul is in your hands.

May 8,

Today was the last day of school for me at Shady Rill. Today another chapter of my life was closed forever.

The parents got together for a little parting program we had planned. Before they arrived, we went over the program as a final brush-up. I wept (not outwardly, but inwardly) as I watched the familiar figures line up for what I knew would be one of the last times in my life, and heard those childish voices sing as I've seldom heard them sing before.

"Lord, we come, Lord, we come,
In our childhood's early morning
Lord, we come, Lord, we come.
Come to learn of Thee."

And when they recited Longfellow's stirring poem, "Life is real, Life is earnest—" my whole heart begged and pleaded with them to let the words sink into their hearts.

As they have so often this past term, Jesus' words of many years ago came to my mind. "How often would I have gathered thy children together, even as a hen gathereth her chickens under her wings, and ye would not."

It was comforting to think of Jesus up in heaven, looking down on my group of children, loving and longing over them even more than I in my sinful nature could love and long for them.

The endless schoolterm has ended. Breathe with me, you faithful journal, a deep sigh of relief.

And yet, already I am wishing for a chance to do some parts of it over, for a chance to be a truer Christian example, and to lean more heavily on God's guidance. May God and my pupils forgive me where I have failed them.

Perhaps I ought to quit writing and go to bed, but my head is too full of thoughts, beautiful thoughts—and troubling ones, glad and sad. Memories are taking me back over the year, reliving it step by step. Oh, what a mixture of bitter and sweet.

What has this year done for me? What have I done for others? Have I, in spite of all my weaknesses, been able to plant a few good seeds into the hearts of my pupils? Lord, grant that it may have been so.

Am I still the same girl that entered this room for the first time last August? I hope not. I hope my faith in God has been strengthened, for He has been unfailing in all my times of need. I hope that my feelings of self-importance have suffered and shrunken, that I can see a little more clearly the nothingness I am without God. I hope I have learned to care more for others and less for myself.

But even as I write, I feel how little I have learned and how often I will need to relearn the lessons of life. What an upward hill this life's road is. How often it seems as though with every step we take, we slip one backwards. What would we do without the helping hands of mature Christians along the way, and without God's hand in ours?

But I must go to bed. Good-bye, Shady Rill, good-bye, all my pupils. Once more I plead with you, grow up to be brave and strong and true.

Good-bye, Grandpa and Grandma, Uncle Crists, Helen, Melvin and Polly, and to the rest of the people I have come to love, good-bye. I will miss you. You will stay in my heart, and I will think of you and pray for you often.

Tomorrow I'm going HOME- TO STAY!

May 9,

And tonight I am home- sitting on my own bed, in my own memory-filled little bedroom. But the joyous homecoming I had looked forward to didn't happen.

Parting with Grandpa and Grandma was painful. I had known that somewhere along the line, I had become attached to them, but I never stopped to think that the same thing had happened to them. I felt mean, leaving them all alone once more.

However, the closer I got to home, the more giddy I became. I could hardly believe that the day I had been looking forward to for eight and a half months had finally dawned. My thoughts were full of home. Would Davids and Ervins be there again, waiting to welcome me? What would little Samuel look like with the dark hair, big blue eyes, and the special 'all his own' look Joanne had written about? I ached to hold him. How I would shower him and little Elizabeth and Hannah with hugs and kisses.

It was nearly dusk when we finally reached home. I began unloading my baggage onto one big pile on the sidewalk, bracing myself for the sound of banging doors, flying feet and cheery greetings that would inevitably happen as soon as the members of my family realized I was home. I paid the driver, and still all was quiet— no faces peering out of the unlit windows.

Feeling a bit piqued and hurt, I walked up the steps and into the house, a house that was deathly still. There was nobody in the kitchen, but a white piece of paper lay on the table. Something about the way it lay there made the tight hand of fear suddenly close over my heart. Something was wrong somewhere, horribly wrong. I could feel it in the very air.

I edged closer to the table, close enough to be able to read the writing on the note.

> Dear Daughter Lois,
>
> Little Samuel is a very sick baby. He has been in the ____________ hospital since this forenoon at around ten. The doctors don't know yet what is wrong. We all went over to Ervins to do the chores and to find out the latest reports.

We should be home before too late.
Pray and don't worry too much.
Love, Mom

What hours of lonely, anxious waiting. And what a relief to see Mom smile reassuringly as soon as she stepped inside the door, and to hear her say that Samuel seems to be holding his own. The doctors think it might be meningitis, but they think he should be all right. There's nothing to worry about.

May 10,

The doctors were wrong. Samuel's sickness is something to worry about, and we are very worried. He took a turn for the worse during the night. The doctor told Ervin today that he might not make it.

Was it only yesterday that I was on my way home? How soon can our plans be changed and shattered. How soon can our joy be turned to mourning.

Oh God, you have the power to take or save little Samuel's life. Watch over him tonight, and watch over Ervin and Joanne and comfort their grieving hearts. Give us the courage to say, "Thy will be done," and to mean it.

May 11,

Today I went in to the hospital to see Samuel. Mom had told me to be prepared— that he had lost weight and looked like a sick baby. I tried to be, but I must still have had Joanne's description of a bright-eyed, dimpled boy in my mind. I tried to hide my shock from Joanne when I saw the pitiful little form lying there, with tubes attached.

Poor Joanne. She is nearly giving in under this strain. She looks haggard and dark under the eyes. On top of everything else, she keeps blaming herself. One of the doctors made the remark, "You should have brought him in sooner," and she can't forget that.

Samuel's sickness has been diagnosed as meningitis for certain.

May 12,

Today the driver that usually takes Ervins back and forth to the hospital drove into our lane, and Joanne got off. Mom and I watched from the window, trying to read the expression on her face as she walked up the sidewalk. Mom opened the door for her and my heart plummeted when Joanne took one glance at the two of us and burst into sobs.

"Oh Joanne," Mom said anxiously. "What's wrong? Is Samuel worse?"

"No, no," Joanne choked out. "The doctor said he's getting better. I'm sorry I—I scared you so. I guess the relief is just too much for me."

Oh, what a song of thanksgiving is in our hearts. The cloud that has been hanging over us is lifting, lifting and letting the sun shine through once more.

Of course, we must keep in mind the possibility of a relapse, but I have a feeling Ervin and Joanne will soon have their little sonny at home again.

Ervin and Joanne stayed here for supper tonight. It seemed so good to feel like smiling and laughing and talking once more.

And now that I have time to think about it, it is so

good to be at home again. I hadn't been able to soak in the wonder of it before.

May 14,

It is Sunday morning— late morning actually, and I should be hopping out of bed and heading for the barn at once. But the rest of the family is still snoring, so I guess I may be lazy for a few minutes more.

I have had a delightfully peaceful hour or two, lying here in the early morning dawn, listening to the chorus of birdsong coming from the trees, reading a chapter in Luke, thumbing through one of my poem books, dozing a little inbetween, and day dreaming. Dreaming about the past, and about the future.

It is certainly more comfortable to think about the past than to wonder about the future. The past is a safe memory— nothing can change it.

Perhaps not everybody's past is so pleasant to think about as mine is. (Even the months at Shady Rill don't seem so bad anymore.) Sure, I've felt sorrow many times, and been discouraged, but I've known practically nothing of real tragedy or heart ache. Even when little Samuel was so sick, the worry and anxiety I felt was mostly on Ervins' behalf.

What if one of the nearest and dearest to me, one of the pillars of our family would suddenly be gone in death? What if Mark decided to bring an end to our friendship? What if I had been born into an unhappy home? Or if some of my brothers or sisters left home and the church in exchange for the world? How would I react? Would my faith in God be able to withstand such testing?

It scares me. People all around me are suffering

from heartbreak, and I am no different than they are. Someday my turn must come too.

I've often heard that sorrow is essential to the growth of a Christian life. Does that mean it won't be able to grow without it?

But it is getting later by the minute (naturally). I must run quickly to the barn and see if I can sneak in beside a cow before the others notice that I haven't been helping all this time.

June 3,

Oh, oh, oh, What shall I do? What can I do? What will I do? I am in a pickle and a pretty sour one at that.

My tale of woe begins on Tuesday when I got a letter from Mark, a big fat one with a bit of news at the end that made my heart go pit-a-pat. He had been planning to come visit me two weeks from now, but those plans hadn't worked out, so he was wondering if it would be okay if he would come instead over the coming week-end. And— since he thought it was high time I got to know his family, he would be bringing along two of his sisters, namely Miriam and Ida.

What wonderful news. Wonderful, but also frightening. The thought of seeing Mark again is always a little frightening, and his sisters and I have never met. What will they think of me? It would be so nice to have their first impression of me be a good one.

These were my thoughts as I began cleaning and scrubbing and getting ready for my important visitors. I had a hard time deciding which dress to get ready for Sunday, because I couldn't decide which one makes me look the nicest. Thursday evening I stood before the mirror and gave myself a good looking over. I decided that my figure was about as good as it would ever get— not too fat and not too thin— and as for the rest of me, well, it didn't look too bad at all. (How I regret that display of vanity now!)

I did notice a slight soreness on one corner of my eye, but it really wasn't worth thinking about. Or at least it wasn't until the next morning. By that time I was a very subdued young girl with one eye nearly swollen shut.

It is evidently a sty. And all day it has been growing in leaps and bounds. Even my left cheek is slightly swollen and my eye is one red bloodshot, weepy mess. I'm not stretching the truth! It makes me look awful. Every time I take another peep into the mirror, I'm shocked anew.

I know it'll be in its full blooming glory around tomorrow noon when we're expecting our visitors. How *can* I face Mark and his sisters, looking so ugly? I won't even be able to act like myself.

Of course, Steve thinks it's a big joke. He keeps coming up with rhymes about *oh my's* and *sties*, and *sighs*, and says that if Mark jilts me because of a sty he isn't worth having. Mom, at least, is very sympathetic, but she keeps referring to how sore it must be, which is not at all the point bothering me.

I guess I'll survive somehow.

June 10,

I just got done rereading my sob story of a week ago. It seems almost comical now, but I nearly let it ruin Mark's visit.

Believe it or not, by Sunday morning sty number

one was losing some of its strength, and making room for sty number two. (Steve claims sties are caused by nerves. I forgot to check the encyclopedia to see if it's actually true or if he was only teasing me.)

Anyhow, I resolved to forget my ugliness and concentrate on making our guests feel at home, but I kept forgetting to forget.

It has made me think a bit. Am I that dependent on my comfortably good-looking face? I never realized before what struggles people with truly ugly faces might have, or those who have deformities, are handicapped, grossly overweight, or are in any way different from the common run. It's easy for the rest of us to sit back smugly, and bask in the fact that we're okay. But why should we be smug? We were all created by the same God, and He could just as well have created me that way.

Mark's two sisters sure are natured differently. Miriam is a few years older than I, tall and thin, with a dominant personality. Ida is a few years younger, and pretty well the opposite in all respects—short, round, shy, and all sugar and sweetness.

Mark and I had a pretty good evening on Sunday. Sometimes our lapses of conversation bother me a little.

June 12,

God, help us to accept this new calamity. Help us to accept little Samuel the way he is. Oh, Samuel, Samuel, what a tiny bundle you are to be causing all this heartache and worrying and tears.

Ervins had Samuel in for a check-up today and the

doctor confirmed the fear we've been having ever since Samuel was so sick— that there might have been some brain damage. To what extent no one knows.

It takes giving up. Our plans for Samuel's future as a bright, healthy boy must be adjusted. It is especially hard on Ervin and Joanne—being their first child. I feel so sorry for them, and frustrated as I always do when someone is grieving and there is so little I can do to help.

July 2,

I got a letter from Helen today. She wrote that the schoolboard kept after her until she finally agreed to teach at Shady Rill this coming term. I'm glad they didn't hire a young sixteen-year-old at least. I wish Helen well. I don't want her to go through all I went through. Perhaps she will know how to handle them better.

She also wrote that Lloyd Hanning gave up trying to fit in with the Amish and went back home. It was no surprise to me, because Mark had told me the last time he talked with him, he had been very discouraged. He said he had been looking for something better than the world had to offer, and in some ways he had found it and in some ways he hadn't. He also said he can sense that some people don't welcome him.

I'm not trying to excuse Lloyd, but I do wonder about some things. If the church is to be a light to the world, isn't it our duty to help the seekers who see that light and wish to be a part of it?

On Sunday one of the ministers preached on that subject—that just because we don't believe in sending out individual missionaries to far-off lands, doesn't make it less important for us to have a love and concern for the lost souls in the world, or to be a part of the light that is to shine to the world. He said that once unrighteousness and hate and rebellion creep into the church, the light grows dim, or even ceases to be a light, and becomes a mockery.

How sad if hungry wanderers come knocking at our doors looking for the light and peace and love, and we shake our heads and tell them we don't have what they are looking for.

July 24,

Davids and Ervins were here for supper. I can see already that there is going to be a danger of spoiling Samuel. Everybody wants to give him special attention. He thrives on it, too.

He looks like a normal, healthy little boy, but as Dad said, the damage will probably not show till he's a little older.

I think it did Ervins good to talk things over with Dad and Mom and the rest of us again.

Thinking back, I'd say that is what I missed the most when I was teaching at Shady Rill— these comradely family meetings and discussions. There is a charm in having everybody voicing their opinions and in knowing exactly how the rest of the tribe feels about things.

July 29,

Today as I sat in church, I looked over the group of people assembled there.

I looked at the row of ministers, bishop and

deacon, sitting with their heads bowed, and wondered what it would be like to be a minister or a minister's wife. What would it be like to have been called of God to stand before such a group of people and preach His Word? To have the responsibility of leading and guiding the church— to have the task of chastising erring members, and making weighty decisions. It must be a life demanding unselfishness and a constant giving up of one's will. How often are they discouraged, and we forget to pray for them?

I studied the menfolk— the expressions on their faces. What were they all thinking?

I looked at the two rows of young boys sitting in front of them— at Joe Miller. Instead of sitting straight and handsome as usual, he was resting his head in his hands. (I heard only this morning that his girlfriend quit him.)

I looked at Sammy sitting beside him, with the solemn light in his blue eyes that somehow makes me want to cry.

I thought of Annie, sitting beside me, of her struggles to accept her father's death, and the loss of Eddie's friendship.

Of Mary Miller sitting on the other side of me, and of her doubts and battles with depression.

I looked at Joanne, holding baby Samuel on her lap, a new look of motherliness and maturity adding to the charms of her face. Beside her sat Lewis Mast's wife Betty, <u>her</u> face looking sallow and beaten and lined with worry.

What an assortment of people of all ages and shapes and sizes. What a difference in people's expressions, in their looks and manners, personalities and characters.

How would it feel to be someone else instead of me? Today I wished I could step into each individual's shoes for a few minutes, think what they are thinking, and feel what they are feeling.

Sometimes I am filled with frustration at how little we actually know about each other. We're often too much locked up in our own little prisons of self, too worried about ourselves to think about the other human beings in the world. We shrink from communicating, and stuff our feelings in the deep dark closets of our heart where there is no danger that they will be laughed at. We hide them behind masks of gaiety, of hostility, or cold formality. And yet, behind all our differences and masks, I wonder if we aren't a lot the same— people of a common race with a common goal in view. Each of us facing our own secret pains, our private wars, our own sorrows and fears. I think there is a longing for the good and noble in all of us, and a need for each other, a need to love and be loved.

If only we could learn then to be patient with each other. If only we would not judge and condemn each other because of a lack of understanding among us.

August 3,

Every summer seems to wing past faster than the one before. If I were planning to teach again this year my thoughts and spare time would be full of school preparations already.

I know I often chafed and fretted under the yoke and burden of teaching school, but now I find myself missing the challenge. It makes me sad that I will hardly ever again be mistress of a classroom. I do love to work with children.

I have other challenges, I guess, here at home. Today I went to one of the back fields with Steve and helped him shock oats all day. It's fun being tired with such a satisfied feeling of tiredness and it's great working with my family again.

I haven't received a letter from Mark yet this week. I'm scared at the way I'm becoming dependent on those letters. I think that strange, mystifying emotion called 'love' is slowly but steadily growing in my heart.

Lord, may my love for Mark not be the kind that goes floating up to fantasy land, and then comes crashing down, but the kind of love that is calm and mature and grounded in yours. If it is your will, let that love grow deeper and more beautiful. May our love for you strengthen our love for each other, and our love for each other strengthen our love for You.

September 8,

I was angry at the world today- frustrated and
depressed,
Discouraged and unhappy.
I dropped sad tears of self-pity
Faced the world with a frown,
And showed it my upper lip.
But why?

Why?
Not-
Because someone was using me wrong
Or because of some great loss,

"It's fun being tired with such a satisfied feeling of tiredness."

Or hardship or pain,
Or because my heart was wrung in sympathy
For the grief of my fellow man.
No— None of these,
But— because
Of a wound to my pride
Because someone didn't appreciate my worth;
Someone didn't notice an unselfish deed
And the praise I deserved
Never came to rest upon my head.
Someone stole the limelight,
Someone was bigger and better, and
Prettier and more popular than I.
Someone was a threat to my image
And all my stinking pride.

For I want to be biggest and best,
On top of the whole, wide world.
Lord, cringing with shame, I come
To kneel at Thy crucified feet.
You, who were all, the Sovereign King,
Maker and Monarch of man;
You were willing to let them mock,
To let the ones You formed from the dust
Persecute and kill you.

Lord, teach me that humility.
Forgive me my pride.
Let me be content to let others outshine me.
Nor let me falter in my work
Because someone else can do it better.
Teach me to be willing,
To be a flower that is blooming
Where only You can see.

September 10,

What a naughty girl I am. Tonight at the supper table I was lamenting the great stack of letters I should have answered weeks and months ago and just couldn't find the time to write. Steve claimed he's tired of hearing me complain about them all the time, and that he was going to wash the dishes so I would be quiet and start writing.

Truth to tell, I was not in a letter writing mood, but I figured I'd give it an honest try. I came upstairs and opened the bottom dresser drawer to get a writing tablet I'd put there earlier. Let me inform you, diary, that that drawer is chock full of trash— some school papers, and dozens of half-finished poems, stories, diaries, and you name it— an accumulation of many years of short-lived writing sprees. Well, before I knew it, it was getting dark and I was still sitting beside that dresser, reading and remembering bygone years. I laughed when I came across this poem I wrote at age fourteen.

SOMETIMES

I wonder sometimes if I'll ever grow up
To do the things that I should—
If I'll ever be prim and proper and neat,
Ever carefully, painstakingly good.

It seems I was born a topsy-turvy girl
With no lady-like blood in me,
For I love to do things that shock and amaze
Proper folks to hear and to see.

And when they scold, I laugh as in fun,
And pretend I don't really care,
But inside, I hurt and smart quite a bit
And my heart cries out, "not fair!"

For I try—I do, I try rather hard,
To reform as everyone says,
But people don't know how hard it really is,
To change my erratic ways.

I hadn't meant to complain so much;
I suppose if I just keep on,
The glad day will come when my oddities,
Will all have vanished and gone.

I'm sure it would be a very blessed day,
For all of my kith and my kin,
And it can only be right for me to fight
This battle until I win.

And yet I wonder if I won't look back
In the midst of my proper ways,
And long for the carefree recklessness,
Of these happy, good old days!

September 12,

The other evening after I quit writing in my journal, I relooked at one of my half-finished stories of several years ago and decided that it really wasn't that bad. So within the next few evenings I rewrote and finished it, let it cool off for a few days, and then with a quaking of spirits, handed it over to my family for inspection. They flattered and praised it so much that I sent it off to the Young Companion editor at once, persuaded in my mind that it was a masterpiece.

Well, today the September Young Companion arrived in the mail and in it was a near twin to my story. It had much the same theme and moral, but alas for me, was put up in much more skillful and powerful words. By the time I got through reading it, my own story seemed so worthless and poorly written I nearly cried. I could just imagine the editor heaving a deep sigh of disgust after glancing over it. I wish I could stop it before he gets hold of it, and cram it back into the bottom of the drawer where it belongs.

Strange how moods change the appearance of things. The other day when I looked over my story, all the sections of what I believed to be especially brilliant writing beamed out their brightest. Tonight when I reread my first draft with more critical eyes, the weak spots are like glaring cat's eyes.

Why is it always so hard for me to take the second or third seat? It should not be so difficult to see someone else with greater talents do a job better than I. There must be an abundance of self-love and a lack of humility somewhere.

Sometimes that virtue seems pretty well impossible to obtain. When I take an honest look at myself, I am shocked at all the forms and faces of pride, sticking out all over me. I guess the very knowledge of so much pride in me ought to make me humble.

How repulsive must be such pride in the sight of God— We who cannot even lift a finger or have a good thought without Him. Oh, to be truly humble!

October 2,

I never wrote that I am working as a part time hired girl these past few weeks for two different families. The job will probably last until they have their sewing and butchering caught up. I go to Ben Beilers two days a week, and three days a week at Allan Grabers. It has proven to be an interesting experience.

The two families have much in common. Both mothers are still young, and they each have seven children, following each other in close staircase style. They are both the wives of busy farmers with large dairy herds.

I got my breaking in at Ben Beilers. A few days of working there gave me a decided case of blues about marriage and raising a family. Fussy babies, quarrelling children, a littered house, dishes, diapers, and one continuing circle of drudgery. I sympathized heartily with Ben's wife Ida, who looks worn down and old beyond her years. I couldn't help but sense her gloomy outlook. Well, in fact, I didn't need to sense it— she told me all about it, how she could hardly wait until she was old enough to get married, and now she longs for the peace and leisure of those days before she was tied down to a houseful of noisy children.

Then I started working for Allans. There were just as many diapers and dishes and children, but I soon noticed a marked difference. Betty (Allan's wife) seems to be happy in the middle of all the hubbub and that in turn seems to create happier children and a happier husband. (A happier hired girl too!)

I couldn't figure out at first where the difference

lay, because in my opinion Betty had just as much reason to be discontented with her lot as Ida. I've figured out that it's the difference in attitudes that makes the one a slave in a prison, and the other a queen of her palace.

So perhaps I'll reconsider marriage after all.

October 12,

Dear Diary,

I'm squatted down here on the floor in the cozy living room, with my back against the stove. My room was a bit chilly, so I moved.

Ervins were here after church and left Samuel here for the afternoon. They'll be back in a few hours and plan to stay for supper.

Little Samuel is in Grandpa's lap, cooing and purring like a little kitty. He sure is a happy little fellow. I hope he will always be happy. I wonder how much he will be aware of as he grows older. Will he realize that he is different and will he mind it? I wonder how it would feel to be retarded.

Brains are complex things, too complex for me to understand very much about them. How can that shapeless mass beneath our skull have the power to think and reason?

We are pleased with Samuel's development so far, though he is definitely slower than the average baby. We all love him very much, as we do our little nieces, only it's a different kind of love somehow, a caring, protective kind.

Perhaps Samuel will not need to face the struggles some of the rest of us do. I wish I knew how to help Mary Miller. I've noticed for awhile that she seems to be holding a grudge against me, and is especially depressed and uncommunicative. I've been feeling guilty for going my own way and ignoring her too much, so today after church we found a corner and I asked her if something was the matter, of if I had done something to displease her. At first she said she didn't hold anything against me, but she is so discouraged that life doesn't seem worth living anymore.

I tried to tell her that life is worth living, that she is worth something and that she must try to look on the bright side of things.

"Oh?" she said bitterly. "Of course you can say so. Why wouldn't you be able to look on the bright side of things? You have everything I don't have. You have so many friends, and everybody's always talking and smiling to you, and you have a boyfr..." Just like that she clamped up and refused to say more.

What would have been the right thing to say in such a case? I feel so sorry for her, and I agree that she does have a hard life, but shouldn't it be possible for her to rise above those circumstances? Personally, I feel she is too Mary-centered. She spends so much time brooding about her troubles. And though in her opinion my life is all sunshine, I have had enough troubles in my life to discover that to brood about them causes them to multiply— fast. I would have liked to have told her just that, and to have advised her to think about others and open up to them. I am quite certain that if I avoided everyone as she does, folks would soon stop talking and smiling to me, too. I stick to the theory that if you are genuinely concerned about other people and show it, they will soon be concerned about you, too.

P.S. This is now after the singing. Mary handed me a note just before we left. She wrote—

> I am so ashamed of how I acted this afternoon. Please, please Lois, forgive me. I can't bear to think that you won't for you're about the best friend I have.
>
> I know I have been jealous of you and that is why I acted so mean. I don't understand myself. How could I feel so mean toward someone I like?
>
> Oh Lois, sometimes I am so mixed up. Life is too hard. I often wish I wouldn't have been born. What do I have to live for? When I see how it goes between Dad and Mom, I don't ever want to marry, but then when I think of going on like this year after year, I'd be ready for any kind of escape. I am tired of feeling so discouraged all the time. Sometimes I am afraid I am losing my mind. Please help me. I know I am not worthy of your help, but I am desperate.

She wrote much more than that, but that was the most pathetic part. I am shook up. It is not fair. Mary ought not to be so unhappy. But what can I do?

I over-simplified things this afternoon, I believe. I still think Mary is too self-centered, and I still think there should be some way for people like her to rise above the circumstances, but I don't think I realize in full how an unhappy childhood can emotionally cripple a person. Or how hard it is for a person with little or no self-respect, to be able to love and trust others, and God.

And again there is the question. Why? Why was Mary born in such circumstances, and not me? But I guess our duty is not to figure out why, but to make the best of the circumstances we happen to be in.

November 4,

It's almost 'summer warm' tonight. I opened the windows to coax in a few fresh breezes and heard the sound of singing come from over the hill. I can imagine the Fishers sitting around the table with their songbooks. It makes a funny, lonely feeling go through me, a longing for bygone days when Dan was still here, and we were small and spent hours at each others' houses, singing and playing. Growing up is sad business.

Sometimes I feel as though I were caught up in a whirlwind and was being whirled through this life, through a maze of ideas, questions, and happenings. Day after day, month after month, year after year— whiz, whiz, whiz. I thought I was a child and suddenly I was a young girl; soon I'll be a young woman, and then an old one, if time and I last that long. My youth will be past before I know it. Something very precious is slipping away from me and I am powerless to do anything but watch it go.

Things are happening too fast and changing too much. A year ago, I was still carefree and youthful, with all thoughts of boyfriends and marriage pushed safely into the obscure future. And now, only a week ago I sat in the living room with my special friend, talking about getting married— maybe soon. Perhaps in six months from now. Six months is not a long time for a little girl to grow up in.

One part of me is way up there, reaching for cloud nine. That part of me is filled with joyful exultation at the prospect of being Mark's wife. That part of me is ready to lay aside my other dreams— my writing fantasies, my teaching fever, the joys of the life I'm living now, my family and friends— give them up gladly and hand over the keys of my heart and life to my love.

But that other side of me is scraping along in the dust, made up of a funny, hollow feeling of regret, dotted all over with question marks. What am I getting myself into? Am I being sure? Have I prayed enough for God's will in this matter? Is it God's will? Is the love that Mark and I have for each other the kind that will last?

I find myself looking beyond the excitement of being published in church, of the brief honor of being bride and bridegroom, of the novelty of being mistress in some little house of dreams— beyond those transient pleasures down the years into the future.

This is the part of me that yearns and cries to be a little girl again, hiding behind the care and support of Dad and Mom and a set of beloved brothers and sisters. This is the part of me that clings to the life I've always known—a life that has been happy and secure. Am I certain that I want to leave it all? For one man?

And yet I think I do. I must face facts and quit trying to cling to the past. I have wandered out of a very dear phase of my life, have come to a door bearing the word WOMANHOOD. It is opening slowly but surely, drawing me into it, into the frightening unknown beyond.

O Lord, I dare not take a step into that unknown without you. Help me to give up my self-will so that you can guide me the rest of my life, until you are ready to lead me Home at last, where the wicked cease from troubling and the weary are at rest.

November 20,

We are getting our first real snow of the winter. It's the kind that fills the air with great fluffy flakes and covers the landscape with a coat of white in a matter of minutes. If it keeps coming down like this, those hills out there will soon be ripe for sledding. Too bad nearly everyone around here is too old and dignified to make use of them. Poor Nathan thinks he has things pretty tough with no one in the family who is interested in playing with him.

Perhaps I should go with him and see if I can lose some of my worries in the snow. I must be getting into a rut of perpetual worryitis, because I'm still worrying about the future and the plans Mark and I are making. I know I'm supposed to be floating around, gloriously happy, and I can truly say I am happy, but I am also afraid. Will I be ready for marriage when it comes? Dare I glibly promise to be Mark's wife in a matter of a few months, and trust that by that time, my love for Mark will have grown to a great and mighty thing that will have drowned my doubts and fears to nothingness?

This afternoon Joanne and baby Samuel were here for awhile. We two chanced to be in the kitchen alone and she asked me how I was feeling about everything. I told her and even confessed that I wasn't always quite sure that the feeling I had for Mark was the real thing.

"Oh," she said. "You mean you don't enjoy being with him anymore?"

"Of course I do."

"Do you feel you can respect him?"

"Yes."

"Do you have the confidence that you share basically the same convictions and faith?"

"I think we do, yes, Mrs. Interrogator."

"Then what are you complaining about?" she asked and proceeded to give me a wise, motherly lecture all about true love and the like.

Her opinions ran thus: (1.) That the romantic fluttery feeling is okay in its place, but it is shallow and not the real stuff at all. (2.) That she believes in God's guidance, but she doesn't believe the theory of there being a one and only for each individual on earth, or that God points out a boy and a girl and says, "You two were created for each other. If you marry someone else there is no chance that you will have a happy marriage." (3.) That love is not a mere chance of happen-so, that it takes time and effort to make it grow, and that true love usually doesn't come until after marriage. (4.) And in conclusion, that if I had the respect and confidence in Mark's Christian character I needed, only I wasn't sure about the love, that probably meant I should work harder at cultivating it.

I admire my sister's wisdom. I even think it might all be true, but it still doesn't take away the finality of marriage and my fear of it. It doesn't change the fact that I will need to leave my home and move to another community. My very being shrinks from going through the adjustment of being once more placed among a multitude of strange people. My heart belongs here. My roots are buried deep in the soil of this childhood home and church. Must I tear them out again— this time very likely for a permanent transplant?

It doesn't change the fact that I hardly know Mark's family yet. (I've visited them only once since Mark and I started going with each other) and I tremble to think of stepping into their family circle someday.

Actually, when I stop to think about it, how well do I know Mark? I think I know him and can trust him completely, but there have been other girls who thought they could trust their boyfriends, but after they married they were bitterly disappointed.

If Mark and I should quit, what then? The thought seems hardly bearable, so full of pain and emptiness. It would be very hard to do without him now.

I feel as though I had traveled unthinkingly, halfway to the middle of an ocean, and was pausing there now, trying to decide which would be easier, to turn back or to press forward— family and familiarity on one side, and Mark and a new life on the other. I have a feeling I am already closer to Mark's side than I realize so I might as well keep going in that direction. Here I come, Mark.

November 30,

I had been wondering if I should give Mark a hint of some of my struggles. I knew that I could express myself better by writing than by talking, but Mark is always saying it's the other way around for him, so I was rather reluctant to mention it in one of my letters.

Anyhow, today I got a letter from Mark. I'm going to copy part of it in here.

"I've been wondering how you felt after our last visit together. I started thinking perhaps you weren't ready for such a step. I hope I haven't been rushing things too much.

"As for myself, on my way home I started thinking of what you and I have started— the condition the world is in and the responsibility of starting our own home. Perhaps having a family to bring up someday. It all seemed to pile up to a big mountain. For the next few days it lay heavy on my mind. At times I didn't know what I wanted to do. I felt so immature and unprepared for such a step. (I'm still not sure that I'm not!) I kept praying for help and guidance and my answer came in due time. One night as I was thinking about it again, a new thought came to my mind. I don't have to climb this mountain in one day, nor do I need to do it in my own strength. We have to do our part but what we can't do, He will take care of.

"As a whole there have been some trials, but it has also been a joy to me to have had you as my special friend. I hope it has been the same for you."

Can I be thankful enough for a friend who shares my concerns and one whom I have reason to believe will be a help to my spiritual life?

Perhaps I have been too dependent on the comforts of home and family, instead of placing my trust and dependence on God. Too quick to worry about the future.

If Mark and I marry, our married life won't be all

glory. Moving away from home won't be fun. At least some of the adjustments and my fears will be bound to come to pass, and at the least we will need to work hard to keep our relationship smooth and strong. The whole step will take faith, but isn't that what all of life takes? Just now I seem to feel God's hand leading us on, and that is all I ask.

March 5,

I must have had a fall out with my journal, because it has been over three months since my last entry. And much has happened in that space of time.

Two weeks ago I was sitting here where I am sitting now, in my favorite position before the window, writing a letter to Mark. Suddenly, I became aware of Mom's frightened tones downstairs.

"Willis," she was saying, "Willis, what's wrong?" Instinctively, I rushed down the stairs, nearly colliding with Steve who came running out of his room. Dad was lying on the couch, a gray look on his face, and mumbling, "You'd better get me to the doctor."

It still seems like an unreal nightmare — how Steve (I don't see how he had the presence of mind) ran to the neighbors to call the ambulance, of the stricken expression on Mom's face as she sat beside Dad, holding his hand and stroking his hair. How the rest of us hovered nearby, too shaken to think rationally. How the lights of the ambulance turned into the lane at last, and strange men came into the kitchen, felt Dad's pulse, nodded reassuringly and carried him away from us, out into the night. (Mom went along, of course.) How the Fishers came over soon after, and we shared tears together, a perfect understanding between us. I understood then how they had felt when Dan had been taken, limp and unconscious, to the hospital.

But, thank God, our story did not need to have the same ending. Our beloved Daddy was given back to us. We all went through a long night, one of crying out to God, of thinking, thinking, and realizing like never before the uncertainty of life. But joy came in the morning with the news that Dad had regained consciousness on the way in to the hospital, and seemed to be in stable condition. His sickness was diagnosed a stroke. We had known that Dad had a problem with high blood pressure, but we never gave the fact much attention.

Dad is now at home again. He is still pretty well confined to his bed. There seems to be little power in his left side anymore, and his speech is slightly slurred. He will need to watch his blood pressure, for there is a chance of recurring strokes.

But oh, we have so much to be thankful for. How easily could we have been left weeping, with the preciousness of Dad's presence missing among us. Instead, our circle is still complete.

The experience has been good for us. It is so much easier to realize the seriousness of life at times like this. It seems we need constant reminders to keep us awake spiritually.

March 27,

Maple syrup making time again. Today both Hannah and I were helping Steve. Both of us need to help outside more since Dad is disabled. Sometimes it seems as though he's not making very much progress, but we keep hoping things will get better. Being a near invalid is very hard on him, especially now that spring is peeping around the corner. He keeps worrying about the work and whether Steve will be able to manage alone this spring and summer.

It is something to think about. At least I can help a little as long as I am still at home, but that will not be long anymore.

April, May, June .... Is that actually all the time I've got left at home anymore? And yet — three whole months to wait until I will be Mark's wife. Time is always so long and so short. With one hand, I'm trying to hold it back and with the other, I'm slapping the reins.

April 5,

Today I dug out the last of our nearly rotten apples from the cellar and cut them up to dry. While I was doing them Dad wheeled himself out on his wheelchair and sat watching me. After awhile he asked if Mark and I would be interested in moving on to this farm and going into partnership with them.

Of course, I would simply love to. And they do need our help here. But Mark and I have already made plans to move to his folk's place, temporarily, until we find some money and a farm of our own. In no way am I going to coax Mark to change plans if he'd rather not. There's no fun in getting one's own way. Perhaps Dad can mention it to him when Mark comes this weekend.

Today I got a letter from Helen. In spite of my optimism, she is not having a very happy time of teaching. It would seem that my efforts last year were pretty much in vain.

Helen was very discouraged — not only about school problems, but also about church matters. Two of the boys among the young folks left home.

Her letter brought back a swarm of last year's memories and impressions. It is amazing how soon one does forget, but a little reminder like this brings it all back — the memory of my pupils and my concern for them.

So two more of the young boys left home? What chance do the younger ones have with an example like that? What will Arthur and Benny Glick do in a couple more years?

I'm so thankful for the relationship we children have had with Dad and Mom. I know that we've been far from model children, but we do enjoy talking things over with each other and we feel relatively alike in matters of religion. We know that our parents love and trust us, and that in turn makes it hard to deliberately destroy that trust.

When I think of all that a home and family can be, it makes my heart ache in pity for those who do not have that gift, that privilege — for the children who are born into homes of strife and aloofness. And for the children who break their parents' hearts by their rebellion when they could walk in fellowship with them.

Home — it's a beautiful word. It is a beacon of light, a haven of rest, something solid to lean upon. It is a sharing of good times, and the feeling of belonging and being needed. It is the knowing that even though your family scolds and uses sharp words, they understand you better than anyone else. They're still your best friends in the whole world.

But what is the point of getting emotional about my present home when I am on the verge of stepping out of it? Will Mark and I be able to have a happy home, too?

April 7,

After a tiptop singing at Uncle Levis, I don't have a letter to write tonight because Mark will be coming next week. So I'll write in here instead.

Tonight was the first time we took Hannah with us. It's hard to believe that my little sister is sixteen. It is a pleasure to watch her blossoming into a young lady.

And to think that I have only nine or ten more Sunday evenings to be a part of the young folks. It makes me sad to think about it. Realizing the shortness of my time with them, makes everybody seem dearer, not only the closer friends my age, but also the younger set. They're an interesting bunch, and I will miss them, very much.

There is something about our singings though, that keeps bothering me, and that is the type of songs that are coming in more and more. Not many other people seem to mind, so perhaps I'm all out. But isn't there a big danger of singing to tickle the ears, and to bring honor to ourselves instead of to God? And isn't that danger intensified by singing the modern-day lilt and dash and dance, glory-hallelujah type of songs, with words that don't have a whole lot of meaning?

I noticed it especially the Sunday evening after our scare with Dad's stroke. I was still under the spell of it all — life seemed so serious and eternity so near. Somehow it didn't seem appropriate to sing shallow, lighthearted songs. My soul cried out for something deeper and more satisfying.

Should we sing songs we wouldn't care to have sung at our death beds?

I've often wondered why, in a group of sincere, concerned people, there is such a difference in thinking. Some have convictions about one thing, others don't, but then have convictions against something else. Who is right and who is wrong?

April 11,

I can hardly bring myself to believe it, but they say it is true. Joe Miller and Lester Zook (Ruth's brother) left home yesterday.

Oh, the grief and the shock of such news.

Who would have thought it of Lester? Ruth must be heartbroken.

What is really frightening is the fact that they were such influential leaders among the young folks. Will there be others who will follow their example?

April 15,

There was such a sad, sober atmosphere in church yesterday. You could sense what everyone was thinking about — Joe and Lester. The ministers preached such touching sermons. One would think it would surely touch the hearts of anyone who might be thinking of following the boys' footsteps. And yet, Joe and Lester heard many such a sermon.

Mark was here over the wekend, and left again. I'm still moping around a bit.

He was here for awhile Saturday afternoon and Dad

broached the subject of our going into partnership here. Mark said he wanted to talk it over with his parents, but that he would certainly consider the idea. He told me later that he had been thinking about that possibility even before Dad talked with him, so I'm feeling pretty hopeful. It would make the thought of marrying so much less frightening if I could let loose of Mama's apron strings a little more gradually. Of course, Mark will need to make the break then, but perhaps men are not so babyish.

Lois Yoder, think of it. Realize it — grasp it. If nothing happens, or rather, if a lot of things happen according to plans, you will soon be married. Mrs. Mark Kauffman. How strange it sounds.

The whole idea is so ungraspable. Mark — my husband. Me — his wife. Two completely different people joining hands to become one for life.

Love is such a strange, mystifying thing — so sacred and so beautiful. So old and yet so new. Millions of men and women before us have loved each other, have taken the step we are about to take now. But never before in all time, has it been the two of us. For us it is something new.

April 24,

How full of sorrows is man's life. People all around me with their hearts sore and bleeding, each with his own cross to bear.

I think tonight of the fatherless family across the road, and of the widow who bravely struggles to fill the place of both father and mother. How many lonely minutes she must have, longing for the presence of her partner. Of Joe and Lester, and of their families, and all the parents who are grieving because of their children's disobedience. Of Helen, as she struggles to teach the pupils at Shady Rill, and of those pupils — with all their problems. Of our burdened bishops and ministers. Of Emanuel Peacheys, who have just found out that their little girl has cancer. Of Ervins and little Samuel. Of Mary Miller, and of so many more of my friends who are facing disappointments and trials.

Lord, so many of my friends are weeping tonight,
Lonely and heartsick, troubled and torn
By life's rough blows.
I long to ease their aches somehow
And soothe their troubled minds,
But God, so little I can do.
For I too am one of them, a mortal being,
Beaten by fears and tears and common pain.
O God, be with my friends tonight;
Let my prayers for them be as refreshing dew,
Let your face shine upon them,
And fill their hearts with cheer.

June 11,

Yesterday we were published. It makes things seem so final and irrevocable.

Today the menfolk brought home a small portable house that has been standing vacant at Uncle Levis the past few years, and began fixing it up for our temporary living quarters. It is a trifle old and worn-out looking, but that makes it all the more challenging to see if we can change it to my house of dreams.

It is situated nearly at the bottom of the hill, close to the road beneath the one lonely maple there.

Annie asked me yesterday how it feels to be so close

to marriage. I often used to wonder the same thing, but now that I am a bride-to-be, I don't know how I feel. I'd be more interested in knowing how I'll feel after the wedding.

I mostly have the feeling of walking as in a dream, drawn by some magnetic force toward a drop-off, coming closer and closer, and wondering what will happen to me when I take that last final step off of firm familiar ground.

I'm happy, too, and excited.

June 13,

I shouldn't be taking time for journals nowadays, but perhaps a few words.

What will happen to my journal writing after I'm married, I wonder. I've often heard that husbands and wives ought not to keep anything from each other, but I can't imagine letting Mark read all this personal stuff.

I must go through this journal and mark or tear out some of the worst parts before he has a chance to get hold of it. At any rate, I think I'll keep the whole thing in hiding for awhile until we know each other better.

I wish I weren't so much of a loner. Those months at Shady Rill especially, have formed a strong habit of needing to be alone with myself at times, to think things through, read, pray or write. I'll hardly have the chance to do much of that when I'm married, and I'm afraid it'll be an adjustment.

Mom read me a poem tonight, called "Little Lady at the Altar" by Edgar A. Guest. I fell in love with it, and stuck it away for safekeeping.

I'm savoring every last minute with my family. Even

though we'll only be moving down the hill a couple of steps it'll still be different after we're married. I'll never again be completely one of them.

The other evening I started thinking of all that Dad and Mom have done for me since I was born, and I cried myself to sleep. I wish I could show them somehow the thanks I feel.

Dad is gaining some. He can walk with a walker now, but I'm afraid it will be awhile before he can work much. We're about used to having him help around the house. Today he washed and dried a bunch of wedding dishes.

It seems strange to have Mark helping here every day. Nice too.

I should be getting my sleep. Mary Anne warned me to eat and sleep a lot so I wouldn't become too run down with the stress and strain of getting married.

June 24,

This is probably the last time I will be writing in these pages as Miss Lois Yoder.

Four more days of getting ready and of trying to prepare myself for the role of a wife, before I give my life over into the hands of Mark Kauffman for the rest of my days and his.

Every morning I seem to realize a little more the seriousness of the step we're taking. Last night I had tummyache trouble, (nerve trouble, I mean) and couldn't sleep till past midnight. As I lay there thinking, I decided that I was more sure than ever that I did want to be Mark's wife. At the same time I realized more clearly than ever what all was involved. I was afraid of my own weaknesses and that

Mark would be disappointed in me. All the other worries that have plagued me before swooped down upon me in full fury.

In an effort to quiet them, I lit the lamp, and picked up the Bible lying on the nightstand. I started paging through it and happened to read the story of Isaac and Rebecca. And I had to say to myself, "Oh, thou of little faith." Surely Rebecca had a strong faith in God to leave all her loved ones and a comfortable home, to ride out in the direction of a strange land and marry a man she had never met. And if the God of all times helped her, He will also help Mark and me.

Today Dad gave me a copy of the wedding vows, both in English and in German. What impressive words— each one weighted with finality.

Lord God, when the time comes for me to answer those questions let me be able to say, "yes," with a sincere heart. Let me say, "Yes, I am now ready. I am ready to leave the shelter of my home, the loving care of my parents, the daily fellowship with my brothers and sisters, the close-knit circle of my friends— to face the unknown horizon of married life. I am ready to give up my girlhood with its freedom and beauty, to say good-bye to teaching, to my buoyant good health and strength, my slim figure, and the wild streak in me that delights in hauling manure and making firewood and doing outdoor, muscle-stretching work. I am willing to leave these and more, in exchange for the love of my future husband. I am willing to accept cheerfully the challenges of womanhood. I am willing to be a keeper at home, a washer of dishes, and a mender of clothes. I am willing to endure the aches and pains that go with motherhood, the awesome responsibility of bringing children into a wicked world and trying to lead them back to heaven. I am willing to skimp and save to help my husband make a living, willing to face the pain and heartaches that married life might bring in order to be Mark's other half— the helpmeet by his side.

Help me, Oh God, to mean that yes and to live it all the days of my life.

June 28,

"Hear my cry, O God, attend unto my prayer. From the end of the earth, will I cry unto thee. When my heart is overwhelmed, lead me to the rock that is higher than I." (Psalms)

Lord, my heart is overwhelmed. Lead me to the rock that is higher than I.

Oh my God, at this early morning hour, the morning of our wedding day, hear my cry. Be with Mark and me. Never loosen your clasp upon us. Lead us, guide us safely through the unknown future. In Jesus' name. Amen.

July 14,

The sun has just slipped down behind the hills and the end of another beautiful day is nearly here. I was canning a batch of vegetable soup today. It was fun to fill little pint jars and know that they are for us.

Mark is still outside, helping Steve put up the last load of hay.

And so we've been married for more than two weeks. The time to take that last final step into a different world did come, and I must admit that I do feel like a different me.

We had a beautiful wedding day. Not too warm; clear and cloudless. A lot of Mark's and my relatives were here so we had a fairly big wedding. Helen, Uncle Crists, and a few of last year's pupils also came. Neither Grandpa or Grandma were well enough to come but they sent along a gift and a card, and best wishes to a 'special granddaughter'.

We heard some really good wedding sermons. I wish......

July 18,

Well, here I am again. Mark is seated beside the desk writing to Dad and Mom Kauffman. I ought to add a few lines, too.

Mark came in the other evening and caught me at my journal writing and put an abrupt end to it. He wanted to see it right away but I managed to persuade him that it was too late and he was too tired. He made it clear though, that just as soon as he had time, he wanted to read it all, and I was not to tear out any pages. So the thing I've been worrying about all these years is at the point of happening.

I think our little house looks cute and cozy. It's amazing what a little fixing up can do. Little by little, it's beginning to feel like home.

We had visitors the last two evenings.

My writing brains are out of gear tonight, for some reason. Mainly, I believe, because Mark persists in peeping over my shoulders every few seconds!

I think I'll quit now, but I'll add this much. I feel thankful for God's protecting hand over us, and for his goodness in giving me a husband like Mark.

July 30,

I must find a few minutes to write this special news— Steve and Ruth are planning their first date this coming Sunday. Steve and I had an old-time chat about it all this forenoon.

Mark has been spending the last two evenings reading this diary. It was hard to hand it over, and I felt fidgety and nervous all the time he was reading. I decided I'd feel better out of his sight at least, so I settled down with a book in the bedroom. At first I heard chuckles every now and then, and then there was a long silence. Finally I could stand it no longer, walked to the door and peeped out. Mark was sitting in the rocking chair, staring into space and apparently lost in deep thought. I noticed that he had turned to the back part of the journal.

"You mean you've lost interest already?" I teased.

Mark looked up, then came over to stand beside me. "Why Lois," he said, with a voice full of emotion. "It's – it's inspiring."

Why do I write this? I don't know, except that it meant so much to me to hear Mark say that. I knew that he wouldn't openly laugh at me or make fun of my writing, but I was still afraid that underneath, he'd think my ramblings pretty silly.

August 1,

Annie was here this afternoon. We both forgot the slight barrier my marriage put between us and had a heart-to-heart talk. I hope it did her as much good as it did me. I seem to be still in need of my old time friends.

I think she's pretty well gotten over her disappointment about Eddie, (he's going with another girl) but I surmised that there is someone else in the picture now. I do hope it isn't Steve. That would be too bad.

I really wonder what Sammy has in mind. I made sure Helen went home with Annie when she was here over the wedding. I think they'd make a fine couple.

September 4,

My dear diary, it's been such a long time since I've sat down and scribbled to my heart's content. Somehow I can't really write when I know that Mark will want to read it as soon as I'm done writing. If he'd wait a few months, it wouldn't be so bad, but to have someone examine the language of my heart before the ink has even dried, is different. Even if that someone is my own dear husband.

Today, though, I believe I'm going to write exactly what's on my mind, and then tear out these pages when I'm done.

That's not the way I ought to feel, is it? I should not be so loathe to expose my personal thoughts and feelings to my husband.

That is one of the number one things bothering me just now. I have been trying to analyze our marriage thus far, trying to figure out why I have this feeling that all is not quite right.

In examining our two months of married life, I do know that they have been happy ones, especially the last while. The first few weeks I felt somewhat like a displaced person. Mark was still a stranger, but when I went back home to my family, I found that I didn't belong there anymore either. I didn't feel at home with the married women, but when I turned to the girls, I met an atmosphere of reserve, as if they didn't know how to treat me since I had stepped out of their world.

There have been other adjustments too, though nothing serious. We have such different natures. I have been secretly provoked at times by Mark's painstaking way of doing things, and I don't doubt that he's been horrified more than once by my careless habits. (To be sure, he doesn't know the half of them, because I've been trying so hard to keep them out of his sight!) I feel obligated to change myself for his sake, but I really hate going to the bother. I'd rather just be accepted as I am.

I've been thinking. At home when we got company, we made sure the house was clean, we changed into better clothes, we got out the best dishes, and we put on our company manners. Visitors were enjoyable but it was with secret relief that we'd return to normal living as soon as they left, glad to relax with just our own family.

Perhaps that's what's wrong with Mark and me. We haven't dropped our company manners. We're still trying to hide our real selves from each other.

All around, I'm afraid we have a lack of communication. I know it is hard for Mark to share his inner feelings with anyone, but, oh, I wish he would open up more to me, tell me all about himself and his childhood. I would like to know Mark as well as I know myself. And in return I long to feel free to tell him everything, even hand over my journal without wincing.

I'm not blaming Mark. I have a feeling most of the

blame lies with myself. I think I am subconsciously holding back a part of myself, unwilling to let go, to no longer be me, but a part of Mark.

Forgive me, Lord. Help me to yield, yield, yield. And lead us together.

September 16,

The sun is shining through the bedroom window. I should be working in the garden. Instead, I am lying here in bed, seeking comfort in a spill of words and a spill of tears.

Depressed... nauseated..... Utterly worn out... A faded wilted rose... There is a satisfaction in describing my feelings, at least.

I know I am being a baby just now, a baby ten times over. Hundreds of women before me have gone through these discomforts and have survived, and so will I.

I had such heroic ideas when I first started feeling this way. I would be a silent sufferer, a cheerful loving wife to Mark even when I felt like crying and retreating to bed. I would not sit around and mope. I would keep right on working and forget my aches and pains by being busy. I would keep on looking as fresh and pretty and happy as I could.

Have I succeeded? Perhaps to a certain extent. At least the first while when the conviction of my own unselfishness kept me going. That soon wore off and it seemed more and more a pity that no one knew how tough I felt and what a sacrifice I was making. I may as well admit that I've been swimming in self-pity the last few days, and probably showing it quite a bit.

I'm ashamed of myself. Such little things irk me, or hurt me and dissolve me to tears.

I have always shook my head in disgust at those women who let their husband's trifling habits annoy them. I decided before we married that if Mark happened to walk over clean floors with muddy boots, if he ate noisily, or if he burped, I would let him pursue his habits in peace.

So, when Mark came in this morning for breakfast and walked across the kitchen floor with dripping boots, I didn't say a word. When he came to stand beside me, reeking of pig manure, I merely choked back the gag in my stomach and smiled up at him. When he stirred up his egg and scooped it down without a bite of bread, I looked the other way. When he enthusiastically crunched grapenuts, I only winced and held a hand over my nearest ear.

And then we ran out of milk. Mark offered to dash out to the milk house to get some more, but when I said that I would go, he didn't object. So I walked up the steep hill to the milk house, feeling sorry for myself because Mark hadn't insisted that he would get the milk for me. (How unreasonable can I become?)

By the time Mark left the house, my churning thoughts of self-pity and resentment were keeping pace with my churning stomach. Whatever makes me so touchy anyhow? What is the virtue of smiling outwardly when I am full of resentment inside?

I feel mean thinking of Mark in this way when he tries to be so kind and loving.

But I must force myself back to work before someone catches me in here. I dare not let Mark read this.

September 18,

Hopefully the above two entries will be the last ones I write behind my husband's back. I had full intentions of tossing them into the flames or putting them away in some obscure corner where no one could find them till many years hence. Instead, I stuck this journal into the bottom of one of the dresser drawers.

Last night it was raining and Mark came in from choring, dripping wet, and ready for a set of dry clothes. I was making supper, so when he called from the bedroom that he couldn't find a pair of stockings, I told him I'd help him look in a minute. The minute happened to stretch into two or three, and when I finally scurried into the bedroom, what should I find but Mark, stretched comfortably on the bed, reading my horrid journal writings.

To make a longer story shorter, we ended up talking the rest of the evening and feeling closer than we ever have. Mark could have been angry or hurt about some of the things I wrote, but as usual, he tried to take the blame upon himself. I found out that he can be very firm. He told me in no uncertain terms that from henceforth I was to cry on his shoulders when I wasn't feeling well, and let him know when he did things I did not appreciate. And if I couldn't bring myself to tell him personally, I should keep writing it in my journal and sticking it in the bottom of the drawer where he could find it!

October 5,

This morning I was washing the dishes when I thought I heard the front door creak. I turned around and behold, there was Snowdrop, Nathan's favorite white kitten, peeping around the half-open door.

"Why, Snowdrop Yoder!" I exclaimed. "How did you get that door open?"

Snowdrop meowed and I noticed there was a blue piece of yarn tied around her neck, with a note attached. I grabbed her and swung open the door in time to see the last part of Nathan's pants legs disappear around the corner of the house.

I unraveled the yarn and read the note. It was done up in Steve's style and handwriting.

"Dear Highly Esteemed Mr. and Mrs. Kauffman,

We hereby, through the means of our faithful messenger, Miss Snowdrop Kittycat, inform you that we wish to hold a banquet at the palace tonight, Wednesday, October 16, 19__. If you desire to dine with us, we expect to see you at seven o'clock sharp.

Respectfully yours,
The Royal Family
(Mr. and Mrs. Yoder and siblings)

We just got back from our royal banquet a few minutes ago. Mark went on out to the barn with Steve to check on a cow that is freshening.

How I enjoy evenings like this when we all gather at home with our partners for a family evening. (Ervins and Davids were also there.)

Hannah cooked up a masterpiece of a supper tonight. She'll make someone a good wife someday.

Mark helped Nathan put together his new kite tonight. (I thought March was the month for kites!) Then we started singing and sang till past going-home-time.

Dad keeps improving, but slowly.

October 19,

I spent the day at Dad's, helping them quilt and finishing a shirt for Mark.

I'm feeling some better these days. Somehow it is not so hard to bear it all cheerfully since I've learned to share my aches with Mark. His sympathy is a tonic.

We have been making a special effort to open up more to each other, and our efforts haven't been in vain. What wonders heart-to-heart talks can do. It seems to me communication must be one of the most important keys to a happy marriage.

We're also in the middle of reading the book, Meditations for the Newly Married. I've heard that married couples should read a good book together at least once a year. I think it's a good idea.

November 15,

Shiver, shiver. Winter is making an early visit, I believe. This old house has some invisible cracks somewhere that let in great gusts of draft. We've been sticking pretty close to our new stove tonight, and even ate our supper beside it. Right now, Mark is curled up on the rocking chair, wrapped up in a blanket, reading Family Life.

There is something about this house that bothers me more than the fact that it isn't weather-proof, and that is that it isn't mouseproof. I have an absolute horror of mice. It seems all the mice in the country know it and have been assembling here to keep me in a constant stew.

Right now, I hear one scratching and rustling under the worktable, It has come to the point where I am afraid to open drawers or to venture near any dark corners for fear a mouse will jump out at me. Mark has set mousetrap after mousetrap and carried out dead mouse after dead mouse, and still there seem to be as many as there were before.

The other day I baked an angel food cake, something I don't attempt often. This one was really gorgeous, and looked like a cake someone else would make. I coated it with a thick layer of icing and we ate a small piece for supper. I left it on the table and covered it lightly with a tablecloth.

The next morning I was serenely putting the finishing touches to breakfast. I whisked off the cloth from the cake, and there, in the hollow of the cake I beheld a bewhiskered little face, staring at me with frightened eyes. I shrieked, the mousie leaped, and Mark came running from the living room.

"A mouse!" I gasped, pointing to the corner where it had disappeared. "It was in the cake!"

Can you imagine? Mark burst out laughing. Then we settled down for a mouse hunt, or rather, Mark did. I scrambled to the safety of the nearest chair and stayed there until Mark carried out the dead mouse by its tail. Then I couldn't eat any breakfast.

Mark thinks it's funny to get so nerved up about a wee little mouse. He has tried to cure me by holding mice under my nose, but I think I have finally convinced him that such treatment only intensifies my phobia.

I know I'm a bit silly, but I can't help myself when I see that flash of gray and the long tail following after. When I can force myself to really look at

". . .in the hollow of the cake I beheld a bewhiskered little face, staring at me with frightened eyes."

them, I must admit they look cute and perfectly harmless, but all the same, I wish they would stay out of my kitchen.

And the cake? Well, I knew I couldn't eat it, and even Mark looked doubtful. So I sent it over to Dad's after removing part of the outer layer of frosting. What they didn't know didn't hurt them, I am sure, but I certainly hope they'll never do the same thing to us.

December 24,

One keeps hearing of distressing world conditions, and hints of a dark, ominous future. It makes me tremble, not so much for myself as for my loved ones and the innocent little children growing up all around us. What lies in store for them?

When I think that Mark and I might have our own baby to care for in the near future, it makes my heart quicken.

I love to dream of holding a dimpled, cooing baby in my arms, one that is our very own. It is thrilling to begin sewing little baby clothes. But how can we face the tremendous challenge that goes with these things?

How can we? I guess the same way we faced the challenge of marriage. It is God's plan for people to marry and have children even in the last times, so what can we do but try to face life with courage?

If there ever was a time when Christians needed to pray I believe it is now. And yet how easy it is for me to live through my days carelessly, more wrapped up in things that pass away than in the eternal. That is what is frightening. How easily one can drift away from God and grow lukewarm. In moments like this, I discover how weak and tottering my faith is, how far I fall short of the grace of God. What can one do but cry for mercy? Lord, though we are so unworthy of You, stretch out your hand and let us cling to it.

January 1,

Tonight Mark sat staring at me for a long minute. Then he asked, "Lois, are you sure that you're that girl I met at Ervin's wedding? That sparkling, nice-looking young girl with the roses in her cheeks?"

I pretended to be hurt. "So this is your way of telling me that I'm not nice-looking and sparkling anymore?"

"Of course not. You know I think you get nicer all the time. But... well, you just don't seem like the same person anymore."

"Neither do you seem like the tall, dignified Mark Kauffman you used to be either," I retorted.

It's strange how it works— how little we actually knew each other in our courtship days, especially the first while. The Mark I thought he was then isn't the Mark he is now. Then he was dressed in his Sunday best, with reserved polished manners. The Mark of then was a Mark I was a little afraid of, one who could make me blush and stammer and act like a dunce.

The Mark of today delights in wearing patched and ragged clothes, he throws dirty socks on the floor, and tells me anything that comes to his mind, with no hint of his former, formal ways.

My Mark of today is not quite so thrilling or butterfly-provoking, but he is ever so much more comfortable to be around, and I love him so much more. For he is also the Mark I have learned to trust and depend upon. His shoulders are the ones I lean on when I am discouraged and sad. His laughter is the laughter that joins mine when I laugh. He is the Mark with whom I can share freely whatever is on my mind.

Truly, God has been good to us. I know we're young and still learning. I know we have much praying and working and giving up to do in our married life, before we will truly be molded into one. And yet, God has indeed been good to us. He has been leading us closer and closer together. May it continue thus.

Lord, let us never quit working, or relax in the thought that we have a good marriage. Help us to remember that where there is a good thing, Satan is right there, seeking for ways to destroy it.

January 13,

A cold, quiet morning after the roaring winds of last night. I see Mark is shoveling out the lane where it is drifted over.

I've been dragging around with a cold, headache and fever the last few days. I'm glad I wasn't sick last week when Mark and I were on our trip. We stopped for a three-day visit at Dad Kauffmans, first of all. We've long been wanting to visit them again, but something always managed to upset our plans. They seemed overjoyed to see us.

We spent the weekend at the ____________ community. Grandpas certainly were glad to see us, poor lonely, old couple. They have aged since I saw them last.

We spent some time with Helen's family and caught up with the latest news there.

I had some good visits with some of the other girls, too, after church. Quite a few of them are married now.

The trip's highlight was our stop at Melvin Glicks. Anna Marie warmed my heart with her brilliant, welcoming smile, and Benny grinned and winked at me from his hideaway corner. But when I suddenly looked up to behold a tall, smiling young man standing before me, I was overwhelmed. He shook hands and said in Arthur's gruff voice, "Haven't seen you for a long time."

I was going over my school memories box tonight, reading apology notes, letters and cards. I decided that the worries and rewards don't stop when you quit teaching.

At least some of my school boys have given me pleasant surprises. Peter Miller, my rebel here at Sunnyside, seems to be making a man out of himself. I hope upon hope that he won't grow discouraged and give up.

February 3,

Dear God in Heaven, above the stars, the clouds, the cold, and the wind that is whipping around the house, above it all is your dwelling place. Majestic and righteous you stand guard over the world of your creation. The wickedness, the pollution of minds, the unbelief, O God, none of it is hid from your sight.

The unkind words I said today, the fretting I did, the vain thoughts, you saw them all, too. Did you write them down in your book of records?

God, forgive me once more. Every morning I pray that I might be able to walk closer to Thee. Every day I fail in thoughts and actions. The days come and go. Every day past and gone is a step closer to eternity. Soon will come the day of all days when you shall judge your people. What will you say to me then?

My God, let all my goal in life be to hear at the end of it, your gentle words, "Come, ye blessed of my Father, inherit the kingdom prepared for you from the foundation of the world."

Beautiful, blessed words. Lord, you know that I can never be worthy of them of my own self, but you have promised that your grace will be sufficient.

May 3,

Who can describe it? The miracle of the birth of one's own child? I cannot. It is one of those awesome events that turn pen and tongue into dumb things. I can only sit here with a heart full of wonder and praise as I gaze into the face of our firstborn, hold his little hands in mine, kiss the soft hair on the top of his head.

Can it be true? Are Mark and I really the parents of this little boy? He looks so sweet and cuddly just now, lying beside me, his eyes closed in peaceful sleep. Dear little son of ours, I love you so much already.

The two of us just got out of the hospital and into our own tiny bedroom at home a few hours ago. Dads all came swarming over, of course, but now they and Mark are out choring and baby and I are alone in the house for the moment.

What a relief to have it past. This has been on our minds for such a long time already.

Oh, oh, baby's crying. And I am tired.

May 15,

Mark is sitting on the rocking chair holding David and trying to get a smile out of him. I told him he's too young for smiles, but Mark keeps on trying.

I'm sitting here on the bed with my writing pad on my knee. It's so lovely outside, I'm tempted to be naughty and go outside for a walk.

I believe I am recovering from a tussle with the baby blues. The other evening when I quit writing in here to take care of David, I was suddenly drained of all my energy. I longed to lie down and sleep unmolested for hours. But here was baby David sounding his shrill little siren. I picked him up and tried to feed him, but he wouldn't cooperate, only cried harder.

I had just gotten him quieted down when Mom came in to check up on us. She asked us how we were getting along, and to my bewilderment, I felt sudden tears slipping their way past my nose. Of course, Mom was much alarmed and wanted to know what was wrong. I, poor, confused creature, did not know. The more she questioned and sympathized the faster rolled the tears, and the faster they rolled, the more worried Mom became. I finally got her convinced that I was just tired. She insisted that she would stay for the night and take care of the baby so Mark and I could catch up on our sleep. I was thoroughly disgusted at myself for making an issue about nothing, and resolved that there would be no more such nonsense from me.

I got a good night's sleep inbetween the baby's feedings, and the next day wasn't too bad, though I was chagrined to learn that Mom was sick with a bad cold and cough. Here she had been up half the night, taking care of our fussy baby. I was determined to take care of David myself from then on.

I did, but the next night was a long one. To start with, David would not settle down, in spite of my feeding him and Mark's rocking and burping him. Finally, Mark managed to ease the sleeping baby into the crib. He tumbled into bed beside me and within minutes was breathing deeply himself. Tired as I was, I could not relax enough to do the same. I kept half-sitting up to peer into the crib to make sure our baby was all right. And between peeps, I worried. I was responsible for this fragile bundle of a baby. Even though I knew Mark would help, the brunt of responsibility was mine. I wanted to be the best of mothers, and fear of failure clung to me like a swarm of angry bees. What did I know about babies anyhow? (Hannah knows more about them than I do. She loves babies and is constantly watching her chance to cuddle one, while I have always focused my attention more on older children and adults.)

I was sure the baby wasn't breathing properly. Once he gagged and nearly choked. Mucus drained out of his mouth. I was afraid to go to sleep, but that is what I must have done because the next time I looked at the alarm clock on the bureau it was an hour later and David was crying. I changed his diaper and thought I'd never seen a baby's bowel movement look so strange. What was wrong with our baby?

By the time I got him fed and asleep again, it was nearly time for another feeding. I knew he would be crying before I could get back to sleep.

And thus the long night inched along with Mark slumbering soundly beside me. I knew he would want me to awaken him and let him have another turn at rocking, but I couldn't find the heart to do it. Mark worked so hard during the day. The pictures in my mind of all the future sleepless nights grew more and more depressing. To think that I had been advised to get solid nights of sleep, eight hours long, with a few daytime naps included.

The next day I managed to get a few refreshing naps. All the same, I began to fret. Those four bedroom walls were so confining. I was hungry for society already, and I wanted to get out into the sunshine and dirt. How could I endure another week or two of this? The rebellious spirit in me groaned and grumbled. I wasn't sick so why pretend that I was? It was probably all old wives' fables, this idea of needing to lie so still when one felt so perfectly ambitious. A bit of exercise would be sure to do me good.

And there was Mom working in my kitchen, more than half sick, and there was Hannah, washing our clothes and the baby's diapers when she had so many other things to do. How I hate making other people sacrifice in our behalf.

I was dismayed at how much time little David took. Would I ever again be able to do anything except take care of him? How would I get used to the strain of all this?

What really lay at the bottom of my depression was the thought of the future. What future would our son have? He is so dear and precious, and I felt guilty for having brought him into a world that does not seem fit for innocent babies like him.

How would Mark and I be able to teach him all he would need to know? Would he see the example he needed in his parents' lives?

By the evening of the next day, I wanted desperately to have a little cry all by myself. I had been up and around quite a bit, in spite of Mom's repeated admonitions, and now I was suffering for it with extreme weariness.

Mom went out to chore, and I was just ready to indulge in a cry when a knock sounded on the door and Annie came in for a few minute's visit.

When she left Mark came in with a cheerful, "Hi, Mama! How's our baby behaving himself?"

We talked for awhile and then he looked at me and asked with concern in his voice. "Aren't you feeling well, Lois? You look so tired and you don't act like yourself at all."

That was all it took. And of course, I still had to be dabbing tears when Mom came over to finish supper. This time she only smiled and said in a questioning voice, "Baby blues again?"

My pride is shaken. Before David's arrival, I secretly felt that baby blues were in the head. Surely if I told myself I wouldn't get them, I wouldn't. When will I ever learn to take others by their word and realize that I am no braver and tougher than everyone else?

Giving birth to a baby is a traumatic experience, a

stretching of emotions, from anxiety and the agony of pain, to the high state of relief and euphoria when you finally hold your little baby in your arms. And when those high points fade away, it's no wonder one feels suddenly very much deflated and weary in every muscle and nerve of the body.

May 17,

Dear David,

Right now you are lying in my arms. Your tummy is full, but you seemingly like the comfort of Mama's arms for you don't want to settle down and go to sleep. Your eyes flit open, and then shut, open and shut. Every so often your tiny lips waver into an unsteady smile.

I guess I may tell you this now, that you are a good-looking baby, in spite of your flat nose and your pointed chin.

Today is Tuesday. On Thursday you will be three weeks old. You look remarkably intelligent for a three-week-old baby, but don't get too puffed up, sonny boy. Mamas (and papas) always think their own babies are the smartest and the sweetest.

Three weeks ago you came to us. For months we wondered about you. How would you look? Would you be David or would you be Rebekah? And then finally you came and you were David.

Oh, David, do you know what a miracle you are? A year ago you were nothing— nobody. Now you are a real little person with a brand new soul.

We love you, little boy. Whatever happens to you in life, remember this, your daddy and your mama love you. We love you and how we hope and pray that you will grow up to be happy in doing what is right. That you will learn to be respectful, considerate of others, cheerful yet sober, a true light to the world, and one of the faithful.

How I cherish these days when we can hold you in our arms, comfort you when you have a tummy ache, feed you when you are hungry, rock you to sleep when you are tired. We would like to hold you close and shield you always, but we can't. If God so wills, you will grow up and away from us and our protecting arms. There will come a time when you will need to fight your own battles and make your own decisions. But I hope that our prayers for you may encircle you as a shield from danger.

For life will not be easy, little David. We have no way of looking into the future and knowing exactly what it will bring for us, and for you, but we do know that there will be trouble and temptations. Until the day your life ends, it will be a struggle. Always there will be two forces trying to rule you— right versus wrong, God versus Satan. All around you will be confusion. Sometimes you will find it hard to know right from wrong. You will fail often and be disappointed in yourself.

I'm sorry son. This is the life you face. And yet it is not all. There is also the shed blood of Jesus that can make your soul sparkling white again. There is His love to sustain you, a love so deep and wonderful that He was willing to suffer untold agonies to make you a free person. There is His joy, and the peace which passeth all understanding— His grace that is sufficient for you. There is His ever ready hand to help you. Cling to your Maker, David, all the days of your life.

There is still so much of good and beauty in the world today, and the hope of heaven when it is past. May you strive to be a part of it.

Be strong, little son of ours, be strong. Fight well, be brave, and the blessings of God will be yours.

June 28,

Today is a special day! Our first wedding anniversary. The robins are singing and the sun is shining, just as they were 365 days ago. And thank God, the love that was in our hearts then has not diminished, but grown.

Late this afternoon, Mark and I decided to celebrate. We packed a bit of supper and walked up and over the hill to the pond with our fishing poles. Even little David did a bit of fishing with Mark's big hand closed firmly over his tiny one. We didn't get a fish worth mentioning, but it was fun anyway.

I've been in a mood to relive memories the last couple days—of those golden-haloed times before and after our wedding. Has it been only a year since that solemn moment when Mark and I stood before the bishop and exchanged marriage vows? Now it seems as though Mark has always been my husband.

It's been a happy year, though I won't try to pretend that it was all happy. I am glad those thrilling but rather difficult first months of getting adjusted to each other are past. Our relationship is so much more comfortable now. We've both learned to communicate more instead of keeping each other guessing.

In looking back, I am thankful for the growing

together that we have done, and in looking ahead I look forward to a more perfect marriage union. For I believe that is the way a true Christian marriage ought to work- something that becomes more beautiful with each passing year.

But— then I have to think, the closer we become to each other, the harder will be the parting if we need to part someday. I could sense the agony Mom went through last winter when Dad was so sick. She made the remark that if Dad were taken from her, only half of her would be here anymore. And indeed, they are such a part of each other that it would seem like a severing.

I know that Mark and I are already frighteningly dependent on each other. A few lines I read while nursing baby this morning keep surfacing gloomily to my mind.

"Someday, someday—you or I— alone,
Must look upon the scenes we two have known.
Must tread the selfsame paths we two have trod
And cry in vain to one who is with God,
To lean down from the silent realms and say,
"I love you," in the old, familiar way.

Someday— and each day, beauteous though it be,
Brings closer that dread hour, for you and me."

July 5,

I meant to do the dishes,
I meant to sweep the floor.
I meant to down the cobwebs
That lurk behind the door.

I planned to do some hoeing
I planned to bake a cake.
I planned to make a hearty meal
For hardworking hubby's sake.

I thought I'd clean the bedroom,
I thought I'd fix the bed,
Shake off all the covers and,
Put on a nice, clean spread.

Well——I didn't do the dishes:
I didn't sweep the floor.
I didn't get the cobwebs
That hang behind the door.

I didn't do the hoeing
I didn't bake a cake.
I didn't get that grand meal made,
For poor, dear hubby's sake.

I didn't clean the bedroom
I didn't fix the bed.
And now here comes the question,
What did I do instead?

Well, I rocked my little boy.
(I hate to hear him cry)
I had to change his diapers
And keep him clean and dry.

I rubbed his gums to see if there
Were toothies coming through;
Felt his head and wondered if
He had a touch of flu.

I fed my little baby,
I had to burp him too.
And 'twas so fun to see if I
Could make him smile and coo.

He fussed again, then went to sleep.
I laid him in his bed,
But when I turned to do my work
The forenoon hours had fled.

I know sometimes I get a frown,
Because of work undone,
But then I take another look
At precious little son.

And oh, I know that he is worth
The time he takes today;
For transient things like clean-swept rooms
Don't last a single day.

And I'm inclined to think the time
We spend with our dear son
Will seem the best investment when
Our work on earth is done.

So gladly will I soothe my babe,
And gladly will I rock,
Measuring time by eternity,
Not tickings of the clock.

July 27,

David is sitting in his infant seat, kicking, waving, smiling, and cooing little gurgles of baby talk. I never knew babies were so sweet, (or so fussy, for that matter!)

It must be an exciting adventure to be a baby. So many new sights and sounds and things to learn every day.

I believe I'm beginning to feel like a mama all the way through. When I'm away from David even for an hour or two, my arms feel so empty, and I can hardly wait to get him back into them again.

Strange that I'm not more discontented. But then, why should I be, when I am filling the God-designed career of a woman, that of a wife and mother.

It is a joyful experience to be a mother. But though I've been one for only a short time, I can feel that it is also pain and heartache. A mother suffers with her children. As Mark said the other day, we are only beginning to realize what our parents have done for us all these years.

September 5,

Motherhood has about as many ups and downs as teaching school. A few days ago I was feeling relieved that I was able to assume the role of a mother so readily, and that it bothered me so little to be tied down. Today I guess I did a bit of backsliding.

It was such a gorgeous day. I ran up the hill to the milkhouse with my pitcher, and the fresh morning air got into my bones. I itched to skip and jump, (what awful confessions for a married lady to make!) help Mark and Steve fill up the manure spreader, swing an axe or just any bit of invigorating exercise that would get the pent-up energy out of my system.

Instead of doing all those happy things, I walked staidly back down the hill, and spent the day trying to quiet my fussy little baby. (I can't figure out if there's something wrong with him or if he's just spoiled. He does feel kind of warm. Poor little thing.) And now tonight all nature seems to be calling me. I would love to take a walk all by myself again, perhaps to the woods or to the pond, sit under the trees, watch the sun inch its way out of my sight, let the crisp evening air clear out my lungs and refresh my mind. It would be relaxing not to be needed by anyone for a few hours at least.

But now David is crying again. It is nearly dark, nearly bedtime, and so I will have to go to bed with a dissatisfied, unrefreshed mind.

O well, moods are such changable things. Tomorrow I'll be content once more to be a housekeeper— rejoicing in the privilege of being Mark's wife and David's mother.

October 29,

Monday evening, Emanuel Peachy's little Sara died. Today we were at the funeral. It was touching and heartrending to see the family's sorrow. Sara was always such a bright, good-natured little girl, even when she was sick.

I am left with the feeling I had when David was born— awed by the greatness of God, his power to create life, and to take it away.

Today during church services, I sat where I could see both Sara's and Lester Zook's parents. (Lester is still in California somewhere.) Both were red-eyed and weeping. It seems to me that hard as it must be to give up one's child to death, it would be many times harder to see that child grow up and die a spiritual death.

The death of an innocent little girl like Sara can not be wholly sad, anyhow. There is such comfort in the thought that she is safely in Jesus' arms, where no pain can wrack her body and no sin can touch her soul.

How inclined one is to consider death as a vague improbability. Sometime, yes. But not today. Not now. Not me.

I wish I could ever keep in mind that it could be now, it could be today, it could be me. It could be one of my nearest and dearest.

Death... Why does that word strike such a chill to one's heart? Why do I shrink from it when it is to be the gateway to eternal life? I have been trying to search my heart. If that still form lying in the coffin today would have been mine, would I have been prepared?

I believe God created man with a love for life. And since this life on earth is all we've known so far, it is difficult for our little minds to grasp the reality of another life to come— one that will be without end. I believe our natural impulse is to cling to that which is familiar and known, to remain with our loved ones. (Since I am married, life seems much more precious than ever, because of Mark and David. I know how much they need me.) And yet there is that longing for rest in the promised paradise, where Jesus will wipe away all tears from our eyes, and no sin will plague us anymore.

Oh, to know my Saviour in such a way that when

death stares me in the face, the sting of it and the victory of the grave will be swept away in the depths of His love. To be able to say with David, "Yea, though I walk through the valley of the shadow of death, I will fear no evil, for Thou art with me; thy rod and thy staff, they comfort me."

December 3,

Lord, give me the proper feeling that I might regard myself with neither contempt nor pride, but as a part of creation formed by your hands. Let me give myself neither credit nor blame for my face, brains, or body, for they are not mine, but yours. Help me to remember that there is no honor that I am worthy of. If there is any good in me, it is a gift from you.

Then help me to see my fellowmen in the same light. Neither to exalt a person too highly, nor to condemn him, but to remember that we all stem back to self-same dust.

Keep me from being prejudiced by looks and personality, but to probe deeper into the heart. Help me to look at people through Your eyes, eyes of love and understanding, hating sin and loving the sinner. Let me love them with a love that will not gossip about them, or slander them in any way.

When people do things that irk me, help me understand the why behind their actions. Give me then the strength to forgive them, as I would be forgiven.

Set a guard upon my lips, lest I be the means of spreading ill feelings.

December 12,

Friday evening. Supper's over, though my dishes haven't been scrubbed clean. Let them soak until tomorrow. I'm not in a mood to do them now.

Mark is lying crosswise on the bed, his little son cradled in his arms. Both are sound asleep. To me, they look nicer than any picture I've seen.

I saw buggy lights going past the house to Dads a few minutes ago. Wonder if it was Ervins or Davids.

Ervin's little Samuel is such a darling little boy, and still everyone's pet. (He is markedly retarded though, and seems closer to David's age.) It almost makes the tears come sometimes to see the children in church go out of their way to be nice to him. Thank God for parents who give them that kind of training.

Well, indeed, just now I noticed that this thick, bigsheeted old diary is nearly full. Only one and a half sheets of empty space left.

Let me see, how many years ago since that first evening I began writing in here? At least four. It seemed pretty hopeless to think of ever getting it full, then.

I feel as though I was about to lay a dear old friend to rest. I guess I will have to get myself a new journal the next time I go to town, though I have a feeling that my journal writings will become fewer and fewer as the years go by.

Um, here I am again after about half an hour of just dreaming, thinking, wondering, and paging through these worn be-scribbled pages.

What is life, and what its meaning? What has it to

do with me? What have I to do with it? Why was I placed on this earth? Tonight those questions confront me once more, as they have so often before.

How often did I feel that emptiness within me. How often did I lie staring across the hills, in front of my upstairs window at home, wondering about life, longing to find fulfilment, longing for some great challenge to make my life worth living.

Have I found that challenge, the secret of fulfilment?

I believe I have known all along what it was. But as one gets older and responsibilities deepen, the answer grows clearer. Fulfilment does not come through being pretty and popular, or by receiving the attention of boys or the flattery of friends. Or in pretty houses, or the goods and gadgets of our age. Not even completely in some noble work such as teaching or writing, or in the sacredness of being a wife and mother. Enriching as these experiences may be, they will not fill that empty spot in a person's life.

The other day I came across a poem by Ella Wheeler Wilcox telling how from the day he is born, a man's life should be "a getting back to God", a step by step, day by day climb closer to God. What greater challenge does anyone need than this?

And when from time to time I get a glimpse of my own paltry self, the challenge is nearly overwhelming. I still have so far to go, so much to do.

WHAT IS LIFE and what its meaning? It is a day by day struggle to lay down self, and live for the good of others. It is a short time of service for our Saviour in appreciation for His suffering for us. It is a getting ready for the day of reckoning, and for the long eternity after.

Nothing else really matters.

"I am persuaded that neither death, nor life, nor angels, nor principalities, nor powers, nor things present, nor things to come, nor height, nor depth, nor any other creature, shall be able to separate us from the love of God, which is in Christ Jesus our Lord." (Romans 8:38, 39.)

And so I commit my life, and the lives of my loved ones, into the hands of the God who has helped us thus far.

Blessed be the name of the Lord.

Our Cozy Little Home